DISENCHANTMENT

C. E. MONTAGUE

DISENCHANTMENT

MACGIBBON & KEE

To
AUBREY MONTAGUE
of Lautoka, Fiji
'*We twa hae paidlet i' the burn*'

CONTENTS

Chapter I

THE VISION

(I)

Now that most of our men in the prime of life have been in the army we seem to be in for a goodly literature of disappointment. All the ungifted young people came back from the war to tell us that they were 'fed up.' That was their ailment, in outline. The gifted ones are now coming down to detail. They say that a web has been woven over the sky, or that something or other has made a goblin of the sun—about as full details of a pain as you can fairly expect a gifted person to give, although he really may feel it.

No doubt disenchantment has flourished before. About the year 1880 nearly all the best art was wan and querulous; that of Burne-Jones was always in trouble; Matthew Arnold's verse was a well-bred, melodious whine; Rossetti was all disenamourment and displacement. Yet you could feel that their broken-toy view of the world was only their nice little way with the public. Burne-Jones in his home was a red, jovial man; Arnold a diner-out of the first lustre; Rossetti a sworn friend to bacon and eggs and other plain pleasures. The young melancholiasts of to-day are less good at their craft, and yet they do give you a notion that some sort of silver cord really seems to them to have come loose in their insides, or some golden bowl, which mattered to them, to have been more or less broken, and that they are feeling honestly sour about it. If they do not know how to take it out of mankind by writing desolatory verses about ashes and dust in the *English Review*, at least they can, if they be workmen, vote for a strike; they thus achieve the same good end and put it beyond any doubt that they don't think all is well with the world.

(II)

The higher the wall or the horse from which you have tumbled, the larger, under Nature's iron law, are your bruises and con-

sequent crossness likely to be. Before we try shaking or cuffing
the disenraptured young Solomons in our magazines and our pits
it would be humane to reflect that some five millions of these, in
their turns, have fallen off an extremely high horse. Of course, we
have all fallen off something since 1914. Even owners of ships and
vendors of heavy woollens might, if all hearts were laid bare, be
found to have fallen, not perhaps off a high horse, but at least off
some minute metaphysical pony. Still, the record in length of
vertical fall, and of proportionate severity of incidence upon an
inelastic earth, is probably held by ex-soldiers and, among these,
by the volunteers of the first year of the war. We were all, of
course, volunteers then, undiluted by indispensable Harry's later
success in getting dispensable Johnnie forced to join us in the Low
Countries.

Most of those volunteers of the prime were men of handsome
and boundless illusions. Each of them quite seriously thought of
himself as a molecule in the body of a nation that was really, and
not just figuratively, 'straining every nerve' to discharge an
obligation of honour. Honestly, there was about them as little as
there could humanly be of the coxcombry of self-devotion. They
only felt that they had got themselves happily placed on a rope at
which everyone else, in some way or other, was tugging his best
as well as they. All the air was ringing with rousing assurances.
France to be saved, Belgium righted, freedom and civilization re-
won, a sour, soiled, crooked old world to be rid of bullies and
crooks and reclaimed for straightness, decency, good-nature, the
ways of common men dealing with common men. What a chance!
The plain recruit who had not the gift of a style said to himself
that for once he had got right in on the ground-floor of a topping
good thing, and he blessed the luck that had made him neither
too old nor too young. Rupert Brooke, meaning exactly the same
thing, was writing:

> *Now, God be thank'd who has match'd us with His hour,*
> *And caught our youth and waken'd us from sleeping,*
> *With hand made sure, clear eye, and sharpen'd power,*
> *To turn, as swimmers into cleanness leaping,*
> *Glad from a world grown old and cold and weary....*

Of course, it is easy to say to any such simpleton now: 'Well, if you were like that, what could you expect? *Vous l'avez voulu, George Dandin.* You were rushing upon disillusionment.' Of course he was. If each recruit in 1914 had been an à Kempis, or even a Rochefoucauld, he would have known that if you are to love mankind you must not expect too much from it. But he was not, as a rule, a philosopher. He was a common man, not much inclined to think evil of people. It no more occurred to him at that time that he was the natural prey of seventy-seven separate breeds of profiteers than it did that presently he would be overrun by less figurative lice. When Garibaldi led an infantry attack against the Austrians it was said that he never looked round to see if his men were following; he knew to a dead certainty that at the moment when he reached the enemy he would feel his men's breath hot on the back of his neck. The early volunteer in his blindness imagined that there was between all Englishmen then that oneness of faith, love, and courage.

(III)

Everything helped, for a time, to keep him the child that he was. Except in the matter of separation from civilian friends his daily life was pretty well that of the happiest children. The men knew nothing and hoped for wonderful things. Drill, to the average recruit, was like some curious game or new dance, various and rhythmic, and not very hard: it was rather fun for adults to be able to play at such things without being laughed at. Their lives had undergone an immense simplification. Of course, an immense simplification of life is not certain to be a wholly good thing. A Zulu's life may be simpler than Einstein's and yet the estate of Einstein may be the more gracious. If a boatload of men holding the Order of Merit were cast away on a desert island they might, on the whole, think the life as beastly as Touchstone found the life in the Forest of Arden. Yet some of those eminent men might find a soul of good in that evil. They might grill all the day and shiver all night, and be half-starved the whole of the time. But their minds would get a rest cure. While they were there they would have to settle no heartrending questions of patronage, nor to decree the superannuation of elderly worthies. The brutal instancy of physical wants might be trying; but they would at least be spared, until they were rescued, the solving of any stiff conundrums of professional ethics.

Moulding the pet recreations of civilized men you find their craving to have something simple to do for a change, to be given an easy one after so many twisters. People whose work is the making of calculations or the manipulation of thoughts have been known to find a curiously restful pleasure in chopping firewood or painting tool-sheds till their backs ache. It soothes them with a flattering sense of getting something useful done straight off. So much of their 'real' work is a taking of some minute or indirect means to some end remote, dimly and doubtfully visible, possibly —for the dread thought will intrude—not worth attaining. The pile of chopped wood is at least a spice of the ultimate good: visible, palpable, it is success; and the advanced and complex man, the statesman or sociologist who has chopped it, escapes for the moment from all his own advancement and complication, and savours in quiet ecstasy one of the sane primæval satisfactions.

> A country fellow at the pleugh,
> His acre's tilled, he's right eneugh;
> A country girl at her wheel,
> Her dizzen's done, she's unco weel.

The climber of mountains seeks a similar rapture by going to places where he is, in full exertion, the sum of his physical faculties, little more. Here all his hopes are for things close at hand: ambition lives along one arm stretched out to grasp a rock eighteen inches away; his sole aim in life may be simply the top of a thirty-foot cleft in a steep face of stone. At home, in the thick of his work, he had seemed to be everlastingly threading mazes that no one could thread right to the end; here, on the crags, it is all divinely simplified; who would trouble his head with subtle questionings about what human life will, might, or ought to be when every muscle and nerve are tautly engaged in the primal job of sticking to life as it is?

To have for his work these raptures of play was the joy of the new recruit who had common health and good-humour. All his maturity's worries and burdens seemed, by some magical change, to have dropped from him; no difficult choices had to be made any longer; hardly a moral chart to be conned; no one had any finances to mind; nobody else's fate was put in his hands, and not even his own. All was fixed from above, down to the time of his going to bed and the way he must lace up his boots. His vow of willing self-enslavement for a season had brought him the peace of the soldier, which passeth understanding as wholly as that of the saint, the blitheness of heart that comes to both with their clarifying, tranquillizing acquiescence in some mystic will outside their own. Immersed in that Dantean repose of utter obedience the men slept like babies, ate like hunters, and rediscovered the joy of infancy in getting some rather elementary bodily movement to come right. They saw everything that God had made, and behold! it was very good. That was the vision.

(IV)

The mental peace, the physical joy, the divinely simplified sense of having one clear aim, the remoteness from all the rest of the world, all favoured a tropical growth of illusion. A man, says Tennyson, 'imputes himself'. If he be decent he readily thinks other people are decent. Here were hundreds of thousands of quite commonplace persons rendered, by comradeship in an enthusiasm, self-denying, cheerful, unexacting, sanely exalted, substantially good. To get the more fit to be quickly used men would give up even the little darling vices which are nearest to many simple hearts. Men who had entertained an almost reasoned passion for whisky, men who in civil life had messed up careers for it and left all and followed it, would cut off their whisky lest it should spoil their marching. Little white, prim clerks from Putney—men whose souls were saturated with the consciousness of class—would abdicate freely and wholeheartedly their sense of the wide, unplumbed, estranging seas that ought to roar between themselves and Covent Garden market porters. Many men who had never been dangerous rivals to St Anthony kept an unwonted hold on themselves during the months when hundreds of reputable women and girls round every camp seemed to have been suddenly smitten with a Bacchantic frenzy. Real, constitutional lazy fellows would buy little cram-books of drill out of their pay and sweat them up at night so as to get on the faster. Men warned for a guard next day would agree among themselves to get up an hour before the pre-dawn winter Revéillé to practise among themselves the beautiful symbolic ritual of mounting guard in the hope of approaching the far-off, longed-for ideal of smartness, the passport to France. Men were known to subscribe in order to get some dummy bombs made with which to practise bomb-throwing by themselves on summer nights after drilling and marching from six in the morning till five in the evening. How could they not have the illusion that the whole nation's sense of comradeship went as far as their own?

Who of all those who were in camp at that time, and still are alive, will not remember until he dies the second boyhood that he had in the late frosts and then in the swiftly filling and bursting spring and early summer of 1915? The awakening bird-notes of Revéillé at dawn, the two-mile run through auroral mists breaking over a still inviolate England, the men's smoking breath and the swish of their feet brushing the dew from the tips of the June grass and printing their track of darker green on the pearly-grey turf; the long, intent morning parades under the gummy shine of chestnut buds in the deepening meadows; the peace of the tranquil hours on guard at some sequestered post, along with the sylvester midnight, the wheeling stars and the quiet breathing of the earth in its sleep, when time, to the sentry's sense, fleets on unexpectedly fast and life seems much too short because day has slipped into day without the night-long sleeper's false sense of a pause; and then jocund days of marching and digging trenches in the sun; the silly little songs on the road that seemed, then, to have tunes most human, pretty, and jolly; the dinners of haver-sack rations you ate as you sat on the road-makers' heaps of chopped stones or lay back among buttercups.

When you think of the youth that you have lost, the times when it seems to you now that life was most poignantly good may not be the ones when everything seemed at the time to go well with your plans, and the world, as they say, to be at your feet; rather some few unaccountable moments when nothing took place that was out of the way and yet some word of a friend's, or a look on the face of the sky, the taste of a glass of spring water, the plash of laughter and oars heard across midsummer meadows at night raised the soul of enjoyment within you to strangely higher powers of itself. That spirit bloweth and is still: it will not rise for our whistling nor keep a time-table; no wine that we know can give us anything more than a fugitive caricature of its ecstasies. When it has blown free we remember it always, and know, without proof, that while the rapture was there we were not drunk, but wise; that for a moment some intervening darkness had thinned and we were seeing further than we can see now into the heart of life.

To one recollection at least it has seemed that the New Army's spring-tide of faith and joyous illusion came to its height on a night late in the most beautiful May of 1915, in a hut where thirty men slept near a forest in Essex. Nothing particular happened; the night was like others. Yet in the times that came after, when half of the thirty were dead and most of the others jaded and soured, the feel of that night would come back with the strange distinctness of those picked, remembered mornings and evenings of boyhood when everything that there was became everlastingly memorable as though it had been the morning or evening of the first day. Ten o'clock came and Lights Out, but a kind of luminous bloom still on the air and a bugle blowing Last Post in some far-away camp that kept worse hours than we. I believe the whole hut held its breath to hear the notes better. Who wouldn't, to listen to that most lovely and melancholy of calls, the noble death of each day's life, a sound moving about hither and thither, like a veiled figure making gestures both stately and tender, among the dim thoughts that we have about death the approaching extinguisher—resignation and sadness and unfulfilment and triumph all coming back to the overbearing sense of extinction in those two recurrent notes of 'Lights Out'! One listens as if with bowed mind, as though saying 'Yes; out, out, brief candle.' A moment's silence to let it sink in and the chaffing and laughter broke out like a splash of cool water in summer again. That hut always went to bed laughing and chaffing all round, and, though there was no wit among us, the stories tasted of life, the inexhaustible game and adventure. Looker, ex-marine turned soldier, told us how he had once gone down in a diving-suit to find a lost anchor and struck on the old tin lining out of a crate, from which some octopian beast with long feelers had reached out at him, and the feelers had come nearer and nearer through the dim water. 'What did you do, Filthy?' some-

body asked (we called Looker 'Filthy' with friendly jocoseness).
'I 'opped it,' the good fellow said, and the sane anti-climax of real
life seemed twice as good as the climax that any Hugo or Verne
could have put to the yarn. Another described the great life he
had lived as an old racing 'hen,' or minor sutler of the sport of
kings. Hard work, of couse. 'All day down at Epsom openin'
doors an' brushin' coats and shiftin' truck for bookies till you'd
make, perhaps, two dollars an' speculate it on the las' race and off
back 'ome to London 'ungry, on your 'oofs.' Once a friend of his,
who had had a bad day, had not walked—had slipped into the
London train, and at Vauxhall, where tickets were taken, had
gone to earth under the seat with a brief appeal to his fellow
travellers: 'Gents, I rely on your honour.' The stout narrator
could see no joke at all in the phrase. He was rather scandalized
by our great roar of laughter. ' 'Is honour! And 'im robbin' the
comp'ny! 'nough to take away a man's kerrikter!' said the patient
walker-home in emergency. It made life seem too wonderful to
end; such were the untold reserves that we had in this nation of
men with a hold on themselves, of hardy uprightness; even this
unhelped son of the gutter, living from hand to mouth in the
common lodging-houses of slums, a parasite upon parasites, poor
little animalcule doing odd jobs for the caterpillars of the
commonwealth—even he could persist in carrying steadily, clear
of the dirt, the full vase of his private honour. What, then, must
be the unused stores of greedless and fearless straightness in others
above us, generals and statesmen, men in whom, as in bank
porters, character is three parts of the trade! The world seemed
clean that night; such a lovely unreason of optimist faith was astir
in us all,

> *We felt for that time ravish'd above earth*
> *And possess'd joys not promised at our birth.*

It seems hardly credible now, in this soured and quarrelsome
country and time, that so many men of different class and kinds,
thrown together at random, should ever have been so simply and
happily friendly, trustful, and keen. But they were, and they
imagined that all their betters were too. That was the paradise
that the bottom fell out of.

Chapter II

MISGIVING

(1)

WHAT could the New Army not have done if all the time of
its training had been fully used! A few, at least, of its units had a
physique above that of the Guards; many did more actual hours
of work, before going abroad, than Guardsmen in peace-time do
in two years; all were at first as keen as boys, collectors, or
spaniels—whichever are keenest; when the official rations of war-
like instruction fell short they would go about hungrily trying to
scratch crumbs of that provender out of the earth like fowls in
a run.

But there was an imp of frustration about. He pervaded, like
Ariel, all the labouring ship of our State. I had seen him in
Lancashire once, on one of the early days of the war, when
fifty young miners marched in from one pit, with their colliery
band, to enlist at an advertised place and time of enlistment. The
futilitarian elf took care that the shutters were up and nobody
there, so that the men should kick their heels all the day in the
street and walk back at night with their tails between their legs,
and the band not playing, to tell their mates that the whole thing
was a mug's game, a ramp, got up by the hot-air merchants and
crooks in control. The imp must have grinned, not quite as all of
us have grinned since, on the wrong side of our mouths, at the
want of faith that miners have in the great and wise who rule
over them. Another practical joke of his was to slip into the War
Office or Admiralty and tear up any letters he found from people
offering gifts of motor-cars, motor-boats, steam-yachts, training-
grounds, etc., lest they be answered and the writers and other
friends of their country encouraged. Perhaps his brightest
triumph of all was to dress himself up as England and send away
with a flea in her ear the Ireland whom the wonder-working Red-
mond had induced to offer to fight at our side. Those were a few
of his masterpieces. Between times he would keep his hand in

17

by putting it into the Old Army's head to take the keenness out
of the New.

Dearest of all the New Army's infant illusions was the Old
Army—still at that time the demi-god host of an unshattered
legend of Mons. To the new recruits any old Regular sergeant
was more—if the world can hold more—than a county cricketer
is to a small boy at school. He had the talisman; he was a vessel
full of the grace by which everything was to be saved; like a
king, he could 'touch for' the malady of unsoldierliness. How
could he err, how could he shirk, now that the fate of a world
hung upon him?

There was something in that. No doubt there always is in
illusions. They are not delusions. The pick of the old N.C.O.'s of
the Regular Army were packed as tight as bits of radium with
virtues and powers. A man of fifty-five who came back to the
army from spending ten years in a farcical uniform whistling for
taxis outside a flash music-hall would teach every rank in a
battalion its duties for 4s. 8d. a day—coaching the dug-out
colonel in the new infantry drill, the field officers in court-
martial procedure, the chaplain in details of drum-head worship,
the medical officer in the order of sick parades, the subalterns and
N.C.O.'s in camp economy, field hygiene, and what not, and always holding the attention of a man or a mess or a battalion fixed
fast by the magic of his own oaken character, his simple, vivid
mind, his passion for getting things right, and his humorous,
patient knowledge of mankind. Even such minor masterpieces as
average Guards ex-sergeant-majors were rather godlike on parade.
In drill, at any rate, they had the circumstantial vision and com-
municable fire of the prophets. Early in 1915 a little famished
London cab-tout, a recruit, still rectilinear as a starved cat even
after a month of army rations, was to be heard praying softly at
night in his cot that he might be made like unto one of these,
whom he named.

(II)

Where, then, did the first shiver of disillusion begin? Perhaps
with some trivial incident. Say a new-born company, quartered
in a great town, was sent out for a long afternoon's marching.

Only through long, steady grinds can the perfect rhythm of marching, like that of rowing, be generated at last. The men, youthfully eager to kiss all possible rods and endure any obtainable hardness, march forth in a high state of delight—they are going to learn how to march to Berlin! No officer being present —and scarcely any existing as yet—a sergeant-major is in command. He is a very old hand. For twenty minutes he leads his 250 adorers into the thick of a populous quarter. Then he orders them to fall out. A public-house resembling Buckingham Palace, but smaller, is near. Most of the men, in their ardour, stand about on the kerb, ready to leap back to their places as soon as the whistle shall sound. A few thirsty souls jostle hurriedly into the bars, where they find that arrangements for serving a multitude are surprisingly complete. Soon they are further reassured by descrying the sergeant-major's handsome form, like Tam o' Shanter's 'planted unco' right' in a chair in an inner holy of holies along with the landlord. This esoteric session has an air of permanence; the sergeant-major is evidently *au mieux* with the management. The thirsty souls settle down to their beer.

Five minutes, twenty, half an hour pass fairly fast for them, less fast for the keener warriors pawing the kerbstone without. At the end of an hour fifty per cent. of the kerbstone zealots have been successfully frozen into the bars. The rest stare at each other with a wild surmise. Rumour shakes her wings and begins to fly round. The sergeant-major, she says, is holding a species of court in the depths of the pub; some privates with money upon them, children of this world, are pressing in, she says, even now, into that heart of the rose, and with a few manly words are standing the great man the extremely expensive combination of nectars that he prefers. 'Were it not better done as others use?' —the Spartan residuum on the kerb is diminishing. Another hour goes; only an inconsiderable remnant of Spartans is left; these are exchanging profane remarks about patriotism and other virtues. One of them quotes a famous Conservative statesman whose footman he was before he enlisted: 'I believe we shall win, in spite of the Regular Army.' When just enough time is left to march back to quarters the whistle is blown, the men slouch into their places and stump unrhythmically home, revolving many things according to their several natures. A child who has rashly taken its parent on trust, and yet more rashly taken the parent's all-round perfection as some sort of sample and proof of a creditable government of the world, must have a good deal of mental re-arrangement to do the first time the parent comes home full of liquor and sells the furniture to get some more.

(III)

Perhaps, in another company or another battalion, some private of relative wealth has felt, in the strength of his youth and the heat of his zeal, that he wants more to do. He longs to get on with the job. So he guilelessly goes to his own sergeant-major and asks him if there is a chance of getting some lessons in bayonet-fighting anywhere in the town. The sergeant-major sizes him up with a stare. 'You're a fine likely man,' he says, 'for a stripe.' He stares harder. 'Or three,' he subjoins.

The gilded youth is confounded. He an N.C.O.! He would as soon have thought of being a primate 'I'll give you,' the Old Army continues, 'the lessons myself. It'll be twelve quid—*for the lot.*' To reproduce the emphasis upon the last three words is beyond the resources of typography.

The gilded youth may feel a slight pricking in his thumbs. Still, there is no overt crook in the deal. The teaching is sure to be good. And he has the cash and an inexact sense of values. So he agrees. The senior man-at-arms expresses a preference for ready money. Agreed too. After one lesson the tutor is frankly bored by his tutorial function. 'Hang it,' he says, 'what's the sense of you and me sweating our 'oly guts out? You've paid, and you'll find I won't bilk you.' Youth is mystified; feels it is getting some-what short weight. But what are acolytes against high priests? Youth leaves it at that.

In two or three weeks the frustrated pupil is sent for by his frustrator. A man is wanted for Post Corporal, or even for Bat-talion Provost Sergeant. What would the gilded youth say to the job? On his saying nothing at first the sergeant-major, with swiftly rising contempt for such friarly hesitancy, recites the beauties of this piece of preferment. 'Cushiest job in the 'ole out-fit! Long as you're sober enough to stand up at the staff parade of a night, that's all there is to it. Where'd the crime be among you 'oly Christians?' (The almost fanatical abstention of the New Army from ordinary military crimes often gave some scandal to experts drawn from the Old. They regarded it with perplexity and suspicion. The phenomenon was really simple, the men being in panic-fear of getting left behind in England if their unit should suddenly be sent abroad.) While the gilded youth tries to explain, without a lapse from tact, that the ranks are good enough for himself he feels a regal scorn beat down on him like a vertical sun. A fulmination follows. 'Then what the 'ell did you ever come to me for? 'Op off! Out of it!'

The youth retires feeling that he has somehow strayed into a black list. He talks it over with a friend. The friend, he finds, has heard something like it from somebody else. Ribald jibes are soon flying about—'Four pound a stripe!' 'Stripes are ris' to-day!' 'Corporals, three for a tenner!' The story goes that a little 'Scotch draper,' the worst drill in a section, has felt that in this newly revealed world his professional credit for tactful effrontery is at stake; he has bet a fiver that he will offer the bare market price of a recommendation for 'lance-Jack' and bring the thing off; the enterprise has prospered and the architect of his own fortunes is wearing the stripe, spending his pound balance on the transaction, commanding his brethren, and enjoying his new dispensation from fatigues. The band of brothers begin to look at each other with some circumspection. They wonder. How far does the dirty work go? Who may not try it on next? And did not somebody say he had seen the stuff pass between the contractor who emptied the swill-tubs and the sergeant-cook who filled them with half-legs of mutton? What was that shorter creed to which the sergeants' mess waiters said that the Regular sergeants always recurred in their cups—'Stick together, boys,' and 'Anything can be wangled in the army'?

(IV)

What about officers, too? The men wonder again. That new company commander who started in as a captain, but never could give the simplest command on parade without his sergeant-major to give him the words like a parson doing a marriage? What about little Y., who suddenly got a commission when he was doing a fortnight's C.B. for coming on parade with a dirty neck? And the major's lecture on musketry? And the colonel's on field operations?

Part of the scheme of training is that all the senior officers should lecture to the men on something or other—marching, map-reading, field hygiene, and what not. An excellent plan, but terribly hard on an old Regular Army not exactly officered by the brightest wits of public schools. The major's musketry lecture has made the men think. He has told them first that, just to let them know that he was not talking through his hat, he might say he had been, in his time, the champion shot of the Army in India. The men had known that already—had doted, in fact, on anything known to the glory of any of their commanders. Fair enough, too, they had felt, that a man should buck a bit about what he had done. Anyone would. And so they had not even smiled. But then the major had amplified. He had recited his moderate, but not bad, earlier scores in competitions: he had given statistics of his rapid rise; he had painted the astonishment of all who saw him shoot in those days—above all, the delight of the men of his old regiment; for, the major had said, 'I may have faults, but this at least I can say, that wherever I went the men simply worshipped the ground that I trod on.'

All this had filled the first half of the lecturer's hour. The men had begun to look at each other cautiously, marvelling. When would the major begin? Could this be a Regular Army custom? But then the major had warmed to his subject. With rising zest he had described the dramatic tension pervading the butts as the crisis of each of his greater triumphs approached. And then the climax had come—'the one time that I failed.' In sombre tones the major had told how five shots had to be fired at one out of several targets arranged in a row. 'I fired my first four shots. A bull each time. I fired again, and the marker signalled a miss! Everyone present was thunderstruck. I knew what had happened. I said to the butt officer, "Do you mind, sir, enquiring if there is any shot on the target to the right of mine?" He did so. "Yes," was signalled back. "What is it?" I asked, though I knew. "A bull." "That was my last shot," said I. I had made the mistake of my life. I had fired at the wrong target. Fall out.'

On this tragic climax the lecture had ended, the men had

streamed out, some silent, bewildered, some dropping words of amazement. 'Lecture! W'y, it's the man's pers'nal 'istory!'

And then the C.O. has lectured on training in field operations —the old, cold colonel, upright, dutiful, unintelligent, waxen, drawn away by a genuine patriotism from his roses and croquet to help joylessly in the queer labour of trying to teach this uncouth New Army a few of the higher qualities of the old. Too honest a man to pretend that he was not taking all that he said in his lecture out of the Army's official manual, *Infantry Training*, 1914, he has held the little red book in his hand, read out frankly a sentence at a time from that terse and luminous masterpiece of instruction, and then has tried to 'explain' it while the men gaped at the strange contrast between the thing clearly said in the book and the same thing plunged into obscurity by the poor colonel's woolly and faltering verbiage. Half the men had bought the little book themselves and devoured it as hungrily as boys consume a manual of rude boat-building or of camping-out. And here was the colonel bringing his laboured jets of darkness to show the way through sunlight; elucidating plainness itself with the tangled clues of his own mind's confusion, like Bardolph: ' "Accommodated"; that is, when a man is, as they say, accommodated; or when a man is, being, whereby a' may be thought to be accommodated.'

(V)

A favourite trick with the disillusioning imp was to get hold of authority's wisely drafted time-table of work for a new division in training and mix up all the subjects and times. The effect must have often diverted the author of this piece of humour. Some day a company, say, would begin to learn bayonet-fighting. This would at once revive in the men the fading ecstasies of their first simple faith. Whenever instructors said, 'Now then, men, I want to see a bit more murder in them eyes,' pleasant little thrills of chartered pugnacity would inspirit them. This, they would feel, was the real thing; this was what they were there for. Then just as, perhaps, they approached the engaging and manifestly service-able 'short jab' Puck's little witticism would suddenly tell; bayonet-fighting would abruptly stop; an urgent order would come from on high to 'get on with night operations' or 'get on with outpost work,' and one of these bodies of knowledge would, in its turn, be partly imbibed by the infant mind and then as suddenly withdrawn from its thirsty lips for something else to be started instead—perhaps a thing that had already been once started and dropped. In the working out of this fantastic pattern of smatterings a company might begin to learn bayonet-fighting three or four times and each time be switched off it before getting half way, and go to France in the end with the A.B.C. of each of several alphabets learnt to boredom and the X.Y.Z. of none of them touched, the men being left to improvise the short jab and other far-on letters by the light of nature, in intimate contact, perhaps, with less humorously instructed Germans.

All this was not universal. Still, it could and did happen. And then the men stared and marvelled. Authority, it is true, had, at the worst, some gusts of passion for perfection. But even these might fortify, in their way, the new occupant of the seat of the scorners. A sudden order might come for a brigade or other inspection, and then authority might in a brief hour become like mediæval man when he fell suddenly ill and the pains of hell gat hold of his mind and he felt that God must be squared without conduct because it might take more time to conduct himself than he had got. In this pious frenzy all attention to measures for incommoding the Germans would yield to the primary duty of whiting the sepulchre; energies that would carry a Hohenzollern Redoubt would be put into the evolution of sections which, through somebody's slackness, did not exist, or the hiding of men who, through some one's mismanagement, were not fit to be seen on parade; old N.C.O.'s would present the men with the tip for making a seemingly full valise look nicely rectangular by the judicious insertion of timber, and other homely recipes for cleaning the outsides of cups and platters. 'Eye-wash?' these children of light would say, as they taught. 'Of course, it's all eye-wash. What ain't eye-wash in this old world?'

It was a question much asked at the time by those whose post-war inclinations to answer 'Nothing, among the lot who run England now' are whitening the hair of statesmen. They were then only asking 'How far does it go? How much of the timber is rotten?' Enough to bring down the whole house? Here, there, everywhere the men's new suspicion peered about in the dark and the half-light. Most of the men were the almost boundless reservoirs of patience, humility, and good humour that common Englishmen are. They would take long to run dry. But the waters were steadily falling. Most of them had come from civil employments in which the curse of Adam still holds and a man must either work or get out, mind his P's and Q's, or go short of his victuals. They knew that in civil life a foreman who thieved like some of the Regular N.C.O.'s would soon be in the street or in gaol. They knew that in civil life a manager who could not get down to the point any better than the colonel or the major would soon have the business piled up on the rocks. Here was an eye-opening find—a world in which any old rule of that kind could be dodged if you got the right tip. It became the dominant topic for talk, more dominant even than food, the staple theme of the conversation of soldiers. How far did the rottenness go? Would they ever get to the other side of this bog through which poor old England was wading? If you bored deeper and deeper still into this amazing old Regular Army would there ever come a point at which you would strike the good firm stone of English decency and sense again? And was it open to hope that in Germany, too, such failures abounded—that these diseases of ours were rife in all armies and not in the British alone, so that there might be a chance for us still, as there is for one toothless dog fighting another?

Whatever else might lack in our training-camps throughout England during the spring and summer of 1915, good fresh food for suspicion always abounded. Runlets of news and rumour came trickling from France; wounded soldiers talked and could not be censored; they talked of the failure of French; of the sneer on the face of France; of Staff work that hung up whole platoons of our men, like old washing or scarecrows, to rot on uncut German wire; of little, splendid bands of company officers and men who did take bits of enemy trench, in spite of it all, and then were bombed to death by the Germans at leisure, no supports coming, no bombs to throw back—and here, at home, old Regular colonels were saying to hollow squares of their men: 'I hear that in France there's a certain amount of throwing of some sort of ginger-beer bottles about, but the old Lee-Metford's good enough for me.'

No need, indeed, to look as far away as France. London, to any open eye, was grotesque with a kind of fancy-dress ball of non-combatant khaki: it seemed as if no well-to-do person could be an abstainer from warfare too total to go about disguised as a soldier. He might be anything—a lord lieutenant, an honorary colonel, a dealer in horses, a valuer of cloth, an accountant, an actor in full work, a recruiter of other men for the battles that he avoided himself, a 'soldier politician' of swiftly and strangely acquired field rank and the 'swashing and martial outside' of a Rosalind, and a Rosalind's record of active service. No doubt this latter carnival was not to be at its height till most of the New Army of 1914 was well out of the way. Conscription had not yet been vouchsafed to the prayers of healthy young publicists who then begged themselves off before tribunals. The ultimate farce of the mobbing of the relatively straight 'conscientious objector' by these, his less conscientious brother-objectors, had still to be staged. But already the comedy, like Mercutio's wound, was enough; it served. Colonel Repington's confessional diary had not been published, but the underworld which it reveals was pretty correctly guessed by the New Army's rising suspicion. And rumour said that all the chief tribes of posturers, shirkers, 'have-a-good-timers,' and jobbers were banding themselves together against the one man in high place whom the New Army believed, with the assurance of absolute faith, to be straight and 'a tryer.' It was said that Kitchener was to be set upon soon by a league of all the sloths whom he had put to work, the 'stunt' journalists whom he had kept at a distance, the social principalities and powers whose jobs he would not do. All the slugs of the commonwealth were to combine against the commonwealth's unpleasantly dutiful gardener—down with his lantern and can of caustic solution!

(VI)

It was, of course, an incomplete view of the case. Shall we have Henries, Fluellens, and Erpinghams at the hand of God, and no Bardolphs, Pistols, and Nyms? Our state was not really rotten by any means; only half-rotten, like others of man's institutions. Half the Old Army, at least, was exemplary. Even among politicians unselfishness may, with some trouble, be found. Still, this is no exposition of what the New Army ought to have said to itself as it lay on the ground after Lights Out compounding the new temper which comes out to-day, but only of what it did say. It was reacting. In the first weeks of the war most of the flock had too simply taken on trust all that its pastors and masters had said. Now, after believing rather too much, they were out to believe little or nothing—except that in the lump pastors and masters were frauds. From any English training-camp, about that time, you almost seemed to see a light steam rising, as it does from a damp horse. This was illusion beginning to evaporate.

Chapter III

AT AGINCOURT AND YPRES

(I)

SHAKESPEARE seems to have known what there is to be known about our Great War of 1914-18. And he was not censored. So he put into his *Henry IV* and *Henry V* a lot of little things that our press had to leave out at the time for the good of the country. If you look closely you can see them lying about all over the plays. There is the ugly affair of the pyx, at Corbie, on the Somme; there are the little irregularities in recruiting; there are the small patches of baddish *moral* on the coast and even in Picardy; there is the painful case of the oldish lieutenant who drank and had cold feet, after talking bigger than anyone else. One almost expects to find something in *Henry V* about the mutiny at Etaples, or the predilection of the Australians for chickens. Anyhow, there is a more understanding account than any war correspondent has given of English troops about to go into battle.

Timing it for the morning of Agincourt, Shakespeare shows us three standard types of the privates who were to win the Great War. One of them, Court, says little; he just looks out for the dawn. We all know Court; he has won many battles. Bates, the second man, gives tongue pretty freely. Bates is not ruled by funk, but he professes it.

'He (the King) may show what outward courage he will, but I believe, as cold a night as 'tis, he could wish himself in the Thames up to the neck, and so I would he were, and I by him, at all adventures, so we were quit here.'

Bates, being dead, yet liveth, like Court. In 1915, as in 1415, he was prosecuting his conquests in France, and his unaltered soul was fortifying itself with chants like

Far, far away would I be,
Where the Alleyman cannot catch me,

28

and

> *Oh my! I don't want to die,*
> I *want to go home,*

sung to dourly wailful tunes, at the seasons of stress when Scots-
men and Irishmen screwed themselves up to the sticking-point
with their Tyrtæan anti-English ballads, when Frenchmen would
soulfully hymn Glory and Love, and when Germans, if the ear
did not deceive, were calling out the whole Landwehr and
Landsturm of the straight patriotic lyre. Williams, the third of
the Agincourt privates, lives too. He lives with a vengeance. You
will remember that he was an anti-ranter, anti-canter and anti-
gusher, like Bates. But he ran a special line of his own. He was
not simply 'fed up'—as he would say now—with tall talk about
the just cause and brothers-in-arms and the moral beauty of
dying in battle. He was suspicious, besides. He darkly fancied
that those who emitted the stuff must have some crooked game
on. 'That's more than we know' was his stopper for all stock
heroics. He would take none of his betters on trust, neither High
Command nor Government nor Church—only one company
officer whom he knew for himself—'a good old commander and
a most kind gentleman.' This one small plot of dry ground was
reclaimed from the broad sea of Williams' scepticism.

(II)

If this Doubting Thomas abounded at Agincourt how could he
not abound at, say, the third Battle of Ypres? At Agincourt our
whole army was just small enough to have comradeship all the
way through it—not the figure-of-speech used by the orators, but
the thing that soldiers know. Comradeship in a battalion will
come of itself; it may be grown, with some effort, in a brigade;
in good divisions it has flickered into life for a while during a
war; army corps know it not, though their headquarters staffs
may dine together at times. At Agincourt the whole of our force
was an infantry brigade and a half. It all lay handy in one
bivouac. Generals led advancing troops as second-lieutenants do
now. The commander-in-chief could go round the lines of a
night and talk to the men; if he should speak to them about 'we

few, we happy few, we band of brothers,' he would not be pro-
jecting gas.

But now——? It is nobody's fault, but all of that has been
lost, as utterly lost as the old comradeship of master and journey-
man worker is lost in a mill where half the thousand hands may
never have seen the employer who sits in a far-away office, perhaps in a far-away town. Two million men can never be a happy
few; nor yet a band of brothers—you have to know a brother
first. A man could serve six months in France and never see the
general commanding his division. He could be there for four
years and not know what a corps or an army commander looked
like. How can you help it? Many generals did what they could
—more, you might say, than they should. They left their desks
and maps to visit their men in the lines; they made excuses to get
under fire; two or three were killed doing so; one corps commander smuggled himself into the front line of an attack by his
corps. But these were escapades, strictly. The higher commands
have no right to get hit. Modern war has pushed the right place
for them farther and farther away from the fighting, away from
the men, whom some of the higher commanders, as well as the
lower, do really love with a love passing the love of women—'the
dear men' of whom I have heard an officer, tied to the staff and
the base by the results of head wounds, speak with an almost
wailing ache of desire, as horses whinny for a friend—'Would I
were with him, wheresoe'er he is, either in heaven or in hell.' But
how were the men to know that?

Everything helped to indispose them to know it; everything
went to point the contrast between their own fate and that of its
distant and unknown controllers. The evolution of the war was
now calling on all ranks of troops in the actual line to put up
with a much diminished chance of survival, only the barest off-
chance if they stayed there year after year. While they lived it
was inflicting upon them in trenches a life squalid beyond prece-
dent. And that same evolution had pressed back the chief seats of
command into places where life was said to contrast itself in
wonderful ways with that life of mud and stench and under-
ground gloom.

It was quite truly said. Of the separation and contrast you got
a full sense if fate took you straight from trench life in the stiff

Flanders slime or the dreary wet chalk of the disembowelled Loos plain to one of the seats of authority far in the rear. G.H.Q., the most regal seat of them all, was divinely niched, during most of the war, at Montreuil, and Montreuil was a place to bring tears to the eyes of an artist, like Castelfranco, St Andrews, or Windsor; the tiny walled town on a hill had that poignant fulness of loveliness, making the sense ache at it, like still summer evenings in England. It was a storied antique, unscathed and still living and warm, weathered mellow with centuries of sunshine and tranquillity, all its own old wars long laid aside and the racket of this new one very far from it. Walking among its walled gardens, where roses hung over the walls, or sitting upon the edge of the rampart, your feet dangling over among the top boughs of embosoming trees, you were not merely out of the war; you were out of all war; you entered into the beatitude of super-peace which fills your mind as you look at a Roman camp on a sunned Sussex down, where the gentle convexities of the turf seem to turn war into an old tale for children.

Such gardens of enchantment were not known by sight to most of our fighting troops, but they were rumoured. The mind of Williams, in the front line, worked with a surly zest on the contrast between the two hemispheres of an army—the hemisphere of combatancy, of present torment, of scant reward, of probable extinction, and the hemisphere of non-combatancy, of comfort, of safety, of more profuse decoration, the second hemisphere ruling over the former and decimating it sometimes by feats like the Staff work of 1915. Among the straw in billets and the chalk clods in dug-outs, in the reeking hot twilight of parlours in French village inns, in the confidential darkness after Lights Out in hospital wards from Bethune to Versailles and Rouen, the vinegar tongue of Williams let itself go.

Of course, he went wrong. And yet his error, like the facts which begat it, could not be helped. If all that you know of an alleged brother of yours is that he is having the best of the deal while you are getting the worst you have to be a saint of the prime to take it on trust that it really did please God, or any godlike human authority, to call him to a station in a dry hut with a stove, among the flesh-pots of an agreeable coast, and you to a station in a wet burrow full of rats and lice and yellow or white mud and ugly liabilities. And Williams was not a saint, although when he enlisted he was profusely told that he was by people who were to call him a sinner later, when as a Dundee rioter or 'Bolshevik' miner, or as a Sinn Feiner or a Black-and-Tan, he transgressed some eternal law. Williams was and is only a quite simple substance exhibiting certain normal reactions under certain chemical tests.

(III)

There may be laid up in Heaven a pattern of some front line by which the Staff in its rear would be really loved. But such love is not in the nature of man. If the skin on Mr Dempsey's knuckles could speak, and were perfectly frank, it would not say that it loved the unexposed and unabraded tissues of Mr Dempsey's directive brain. Hotspur, in deathless words, has aired the eternal grudge of the combatant soldier against the Brass Hat—

> *I remember, when the fight was done,*
> *When I was dry with rage and extreme toil,*
> *Breathless and faint, leaning upon my sword,*
> *Came there a certain lord, neat and trimly dressed,*
> *Fresh as a bridegroom.*

So the jaundiced narrative flows on and on, doing the fullest justice on record to some of the main heads of the front line's immemorial distaste for the Staff—for its too Olympian line of comment upon the vulgar minutiæ of combat, its offensively manifest facilities for getting a good shave, its fertility in gratuitous advice of an imperfectly practical kind, and its occasional lapses from grace in speaking of the men, the beloved men, the objects of every good combatant officer's jealous and wrathful affection.

Or, again, you might say that a Staff is a trouser-button, which there are few to praise while it goes on with its work, and very few to abstain from cursing when it comes off. When a Staff's work is done well the front line only feels as if Nature were marching, without actual molestation, along some beneficent course of her own. But when some one slips up, and half a brigade is left to itself in a cold, cold world encircled by Germans, the piercing eye of the front line perceives in a moment how pitifully ill the Brass Hats deserve of their country. If you are an infantry-man the Brass Hats above you are, in your sight, a kind of *ex officio* children of perdition, like your own gunners. As long as your own gunners go on achieving the masterpiece of mathematics that is required to confine the incidence of their shells to the enemy you feel that, just for the moment, a gunner's rich natural endowment of original sin is not telling for all it is worth. But some day the frailty of man or of metal causes a short one to drop once again among you and your friends; and then you are mightily refreshed and confirmed in the stern Calvinistic faith of the infantry that there are chosen vessels of grace and also chosen vessels of homicidal mania.

If man, in all his wars, is predestined never to love and trust his Brass Hats, least of all can he struggle against this disability when he is warring in trenches. Why? Because trench life is very domestic, highly atomic. Its atom, or unit, like that of slum life, is the jealously close, exclusive, contriving life of a family housed in an urban cellar. During the years of trench war a man seldom saw the whole of his company at a time. Our total host might be two millions strong, or ten millions; whatever its size a man's world was that of his section—at most, his platoon; all that mattered much to him was the one little boatload of castaways with whom he was marooned on a desert island and making shift to keep off the weather and any sudden attack of wild beasts. Absorbed in the primitive job of keeping alive on earth naked except in the matter of food, they became, like other primitive men, family separatists. Any odd chattel that each trench household acquired served as an extra dab of cement for the household's internal affections, as well as a possible *casus belli* against the unblessed outsiders who dared to cast upon it the eye of desire. A brazier with three equal legs would be coveted by a whole company. Once a platoon acquired a broken, but just practicable, arm-chair; not exactly a stronghold of luxury; rather a freakish wave of her banner; and this symbol of lost joys was borne, at great inconvenience, from sector to sector of the front, amidst the affected derision of other platoons—veiling what was well understood to be envy. It was like the grim, ineffusive

B

spiritual cohesion of a Scottish family soldered together to keep out the world.

Constantly jammed up against one another, every man in each of these isolated knots of adventurers came to be seen by the rest for what he was worth, with the drastic clearness of open-eyed husbands and wives of long standing. They had domesticated the Day of Judgment. Many old valuations had to go by the board; some great home reputations wilted surprisingly; stones that the builders of public opinion on Salisbury Plain had confidently rejected found their way up to the heads of corners. Officers, watched almost as closely, were sorted out by the minds of the men into themes for contemptuous silence, objects of the love that doeth and beareth all things, and cases of Not Proven Yet. The cutting equity of this family council was bracing. It got the best out of everybody in whom there was anything. Imagine a similar overhauling of public life here! And the size of the scrap-heap! But to the outer world, which it did not half know, the tribunal was harsh, and harshest of all to the outer and upper world of army principalities and powers.

These were, to it, the untested, unsifted, 'the crowd that was never put through it.' There were presumptions against them, besides. They were akin, in the combatant's sight, to the elfish gods that had ruled and bedevilled his training at home. They were of the breed of the wasters, the misorganizers, the beauties who sent his battalion out from the Wiltshire downs to Bruay along a course of gigantic zigzags, like a yacht beating up in the teeth of a wind, first running far south to Havre, then north to near the German Ocean, and then going about and opening out again upon the southward tack until Bruay was struck; for it was, indeed, along a trajectory somewhat like that of an actual flash of lightning in some quaint engraving that Britain hurled at the enemy many of her new thunderbolts of war. Also, they stood in the shoes of the men who in French's day had sent platoon commanders to take woods and quarries not marked on their maps. And they were the men who, when troops had been marching twelve miles in full kit on the high-cambered, heavily greased Flanders setts in the rain, would appear on the roadside turf round a blind corner, sitting chubby and sleek on fresh horses, and say that the marching was damned bad and troops must go back to-morrow and do it again. But the chief count was the first—that they had not all gone through the mill; that they lived in a world in which all the respectable old bubbles, pricked elsewhere, were still fat and shining, where all the old bluffs were uncalled and still going strong, and the wangler could still inherit the earth and eye-wash reign happy and glorious.

Not a judgment wholly just. But not one contemptible either; for, wherever it ended, it set out from the right idea of judging a man only by what he was worth and what he could do. And, just or not, it was real; it influenced men's acts, not to the extent of losing us the war, but to that of helping to send the winners home possessed with that contemptuous impatience of authority which has already thrown out of gear so much of the pre-war machinery for regulating the joint action of mankind.

(IV)

There was yet another special check during the war upon love and respect for the higher commands. There were so many things of moment which they were the last to find out. Time after time the great ones of this world were seen to be walking in darkness long after the lowly had seen a great light. While the appointed brains of our army were still swearing hard by the rifle, and nothing but it, as the infantry's friend, a more saving truth had entered in at the lowly door of the infantry's mind. Ignoring all that at Aldershot they had learnt to be sacred, they contumaciously saw that so long as you stand in a hole deeper than you are tall you never will hit with a rifle-bullet another man standing in just such another hole twenty yards off. But also—divine idea! —that you can throw a tin can from your hole into his.

In England the mighty had taken a great deal of pains to teach the New Army always to parry the thrust of its enemy's bayonet first, and only then to get in its own. A fine, stately procedure it was when taught by an exemplary Regular Army instructor fully resolved that, whatever Shelley may say, no part of any movement must mingle in any other part's being. In France, and no doubt on other fronts too, it abruptly dawned on those whose style this formalist had moulded, more or less, that a second German or Turk was apt to cut in before the appointed ritual of debate with the first could be carried to a happy end. Illicit abridgments followed, attended by contumacious reflections.

Whatever, again, was august in Canadian life and affairs was bent in 1914 upon arming Canadian troops with what was indeed, by a long chalk, the pick of all match-shooting rifles. It was the last word of man in his struggle against the caprices of barometric and thermometric pressures on ranges. And it was to show a purblind Europe, among other things, that Sam Hughes was the man and that wisdom would die with him. Yet hardly had its use, in wrath, begun when there broke upon the untutored Canadian foot-soldier a revelation withheld from the Hugheses of this world. He perceived that the enemy, in his perversity, did not intend to stand up on a skyline a thousand yards off to be shot with all the refinements of science; point-blank was going to be the only range, except for a few specialists; rapidity of fire would matter more than precision; and all the super-subtle appliances tending to triumphs at Bisley would here be no better than aids to the picking of mud from trench walls as the slung rifle joggled against them.

The great did not turn these truths of mean origin right away from the door. They would quite often take a discovery in. Only there was no running to greet it.

There was no hurry in their hands,
No hurry in their feet.

Like smells that originate in the kitchen and work their way up by degrees to the best bedroom the new revelations of war ascended slowly from floor to floor of the hierarchy. They did arrive in the end. The Canadians got, in the end, a rifle not too great and good for business. By the third year of the war the infantry schools at the base were teaching drafts from home to use the bayonet as troops in the line had taught themselves to use it in the second. The frowning down of the tanks can hardly have lasted a year. The Stokes gun was not blackballed for good. It was not for all time, but only for what seemed to them like an age, that our troops had to keep off the well-found enemy bomber with bombs that they made of old jam tins, wire, a little gun-cotton, a little time fuse, and some bits of sharp stone, old iron, or anything hard that was lying about, with earth to fill in;

the higher powers did the thing well in the end; they came down handsomely at last; in the next life the Mills bomb alone should be good for at least a night out once a year on an iceberg to some War Office brave who would not see it killed in the cradle.

And yet authority wore, in the eyes of its troops in the field, an inexpert air—sublime, benevolent, but somehow inexpert. They had begun to notice it even before leaving England. Imagine the headquarters Staff of a district command watching a test for battalion bombing officers and sergeants at the close of a divisional bombing course in 1915: the instructor in charge a quick-witted Regular N.C.O. who has shone at Loos and is now decorated, commissioned, slightly shell-shocked, and sent home to teach, full of the new craft and subtlety of trench war; the pupils all picked for the job and devouringly keen, half of them old cricketers, all able-bodied, and all now able, after hard practice during the course, to drop a bomb on to any desired square yard within thirty-five yards of their stance; and then the Staff, tropically dazzling in their red and gold, august beyond words, but genial, benign, encouraging, only too ready to praise things that they would see to be easy if only they knew more about them and were not like middle-aged mothers watching their offspring at football—so a profane bombing sergeant describes them that night to his mess.

(V)

'Your Old Army's all bloody born amatoors,' an Australian of ripe war experience remarked with some frankness in France. His immediate occasion for generalizing so rashly was somebody's slip in passing certain grenades as good for field use. Most of our hand rifle grenades undoubtedly were. If anything they were too fine for it, too fit to beautify drawing-rooms as well. One *objet d'art*, a delight to the eye, was said to cost its country one pound five as against the two francs for which France was composing an angel of death less pretty but equally virtuous. Still, ours would kill, if you had the heart to break up an object so fair. But the batch that made the Australian blaspheme, though good in design, were mismade. They were made as if the people who made them had not guessed what they were for.

As you know, the outside of most kinds of grenades is a thick metal case serrated with deeply-cut lines that cross each other like those more shallow sunk lines on crocodile-leather, only at right angles. These lines of weakness, cut into the metal, mark out almost the whole of the case into little squares standing up in relief, sixteen or thirty-two or forty-eight or seventy-two according to type. The burst, if all goes well, attacks the lines of weakness, cuts them right through, and so disperses all the little squares of brass, cast-iron, or steel radially as flying bits of shrapnel. What led the Australian to sin was that this batch had come out to France with their lines of weakness cut not half as deep as they should be. The burst only ripped the case open without breaking it up. It had been lovely in life, and in death it was not divided. It just gave a jump, the length of a frog's, and presented the foe with a cheap good souvenir, reassuring besides.

There must have been a good many thousands of these. They may have done good—perhaps won a good-conduct mark to some War Office hero for rushing them out in good time to the front; perhaps assisted some politician to feel that he was riding a whirlwind and directing a storm, solving munition crises and winning the war. All human happiness counts. In France, if the physical effects of their detonation were poor, the moral reverberations which followed were lively. A bombing sergeant, sent down the line for a rest and instructing new drafts in a hollow among the sand dunes at Etaples well out of authority's hearing, would start his lecture by holding one of them up and saying: 'This 'ere, men, is a damn bad grenade. But it's all that the bloody tailors give you to work with. So just pay attention to me.' And then he would go on to pour out his cornucopia of tips, fruits of empiric research, for doing what somebody's slackness or folly had made it so much less easy to do.

(VI)

Whenever you passed from east to west across the British zone during the war you would find somebody saying with fervour that somebody else, a little more to the west and a little higher in rank, had not even learnt his job well enough to keep out of the way. Subalterns, who by some odd arrangement of flukes had come through our attacks on the Somme in 1916 and in Artois and Flanders next year, would hoot at the notion—it had a vogue with part of the Staff in a tranquil far west—that the way to get on with the war was to raise a more specific thirst for blood in the private. Battalion commanders did not soon tire of telling how in the busiest days of big battles the unseen powers would pester them for instant returns of the number of shovels they had, or of the number of men who in civil life had been fitters, or had been moulders. Brigadiers would savagely wonder aloud whether it ever occurred to a higher command that to make little attack after little attack, each on a narrow, one-brigade front, was merely to ask to have each attack squashed flat in its turn by a fan-like convergence of fire from the enemy's guns on both flanks, not to speak of supports. The day the bad turn came for us, in the two-chaptered battle of Cambrai, an officer on the Staff of one of the worst-hit divisions observed: 'Our attitude is just "we told you so." ' When the good turn in the war had come the next summer there was a day, not so good as the rest, when two squadrons of horse were sent to charge, in column, up a straight, treeless rising road for half a mile and take a little wood at the top. There were many machine-guns in the wood—how could there not have been?—and the whole air sang with warnings of that. No horse or man either got to the wood or came back. They were all in a few seconds lying in the white dust, almost in the order they rode in, the officer in command a little ahead of the rest. It looked, in its formal completeness, like a thing acted, a kinema play showing a part of Sennacherib's army on which the angel had breathed. On the road back from the place I met a corps commander—a great man at his work. When he heard his face crumpled up for a moment—he was a soft-hearted man. 'Another of those damned cavalry follies!' he growled. His voice had the scorn that the man who is versed in to-day's practice feels for the men who still move among yesterday's theories. So it was, from east to west, all the way.

All the wise men were not in the east. It was the fault of the war, the outlandish, innovatory war that did not conform to the proper text-books as it ought to have done; an unimagined war of flankless armies scratching each other's faces across an endless thorn hedge, not dreamt of in Staff College philosophy; a war that was always putting out of date the best that had been known and thought and invented, always sending everyone to school again; unkind, above all, to us who, if well-to-do, bring up our young to have a proper respect for the past and to feel that if yesterday's parasol will not keep out the rain of to-day, then it ought to, and no one can blame them for using it.

(VII)

Yet the men in the line talked, and so did the subalterns, most of whom had been in the ranks, now that the war ran into years. Soldiers have endless occasions for talk. Being seldom alone, and having to hold their tongues sometimes, they talk all the time that they can. And most of their talk was sour and scornful. Ever since their enlistment there had been running down in them one of the springs of health in the life of a country. An unprecedented number of the most healthy, high-spirited, and nationally valuable Englishmen in the prime of life were telling one another that, among those whom they had hitherto taken more or less completely on trust as their 'betters,' things were going on which must make the war harder for us to win; while they, the common people, cared with all their hearts about saving Belguim and France, those betters, so placed that they could do more to that end if they would, seemed to be caring, on the whole, less— shouting and gesticulating enough, but ready to give up less of what was pleasant and to do less of what was hard, and perhaps not able to do much at their best. Colonel Repington's friends, with their scented baths, their prime vintages, and their mutinous chatter, were not actually seen; but there was a bad smell about; the air stank of bad work in high places.

Most of our N.C.O.'s and men in the field had come to feel that it was left to them and to the soundest regimental officers to pull the foundered rulers of England and heads of the army through the scrape. They assumed now that while they were doing this job they must expect to be crawled upon by all the vermin bred in the dark places of a rich country vulgarly governed. They were well on their guard by this time against expressing any thoroughgoing faith in anything or anybody, or incurring any suspicion of dreaming that such a faith was likely to animate others; a man was a fool if he imagined that anyone set over him was not looking after number one; the patriotism of the press was bunkum, screening all sorts of queer games; the eloquence of patriotic orators was just a smoke barrage to cover their little manœuvres against one another; the red tabs of the Staff were the 'Red Badge of Funk'; a hospital ward full of sick men would exchange, when left to themselves, vitriolic surmises about the extravagant pay that the nurses were probably getting, and go on to suggest what vast profits the Y.M.C.A. must be making out of its huts. Wherever the contrary had not been proved to their own senses, the slacking, self-seeking and shirking that had muddled and spoilt their own training for war until they were put, half-trained, in the hottest of the fire must be assumed to be in authority everywhere.

Long ago, perhaps, the commons of England may, on the whole, have accepted the view that while they were the fists of her army there was a strong brain somewhere behind, as good at its job as the fists were at theirs; that above them, using them for the best, mind was enthroned, mind the deviser, adapter, foreseer, the finder of ever new means to new ends, mind which knew better than fists, and from which, in any time of trial, all good counsels and provident works were sure to proceed. If so, the faith of the general mass of the English common people in any such division of functions was now pretty near its last kick. The lions felt they had found out the asses. They would not try to throw off the lead of the asses just then: you cannot re-organize a fire-brigade in the midst of a fire. That had to wait. They worked grimly on at the job of the moment, resigned for the present to seeing all the things go ill which the great ones of their world ought to have caused to go well. For themselves, in each of their units, they saw what was coming. Some day soon they would be put into an attack and would come out with half their numbers or, perhaps, two-thirds, and nothing gained for England, perhaps because some old Regular in his youth had pre-ferred playing polo to learning his job. The rest would be brought up to strength with half-trained drafts and then put in again, and the process would go on over and over again until our commanders learnt war, and then perhaps we might win, if any of us were left.

While so many things were shaken one thing that held fast was the men's will to win. It may have changed from the first lyric-hearted enthusiasm. But it was a dour and inveterate will. At the worst most of the men fully meant to go down killing for all they were worth. And there was just a hope that in Germany, too, such default as they saw on our side was the rule; it was, perhaps, a disease of all armies and countries, not of ours alone; there might thus be a chance for us still. On that chance they still worked away with a sullen ardour that no muddling or sloth in high places could wholly damp down. Many of them were like children clinging with a cross crankiness to a hobby of learning to read in a school where some of the teachers were good, but some could not read themselves, and others could read but preferred other occupations to teaching.

All were so deeply absorbed in winning that no practical upshot of all their new thoughts about England's diseases was yet, as far as I could perceive, taking shape in their minds. On that side their mood was merely one of postponement, somewhat menacing in its form, but still postponement. 'We've *got* to win first. Then——? But we've got to win first.' They were almost exactly the words in which most German prisoners, till 1918, expressed their own feelings about the old rulers of Germany.

Chapter IV

TEDIUM

(I)

A BOOK may be bad and yet tell you much. Lately I came across such a book. It is surely one of the crossest books ever written. Its author fought in France, in the ranks, for a good many months of the war. He must have been one of the men who make sergeants grey—a 'proper lawyer,' as Regulars call the type which a cotton district labels as 'self-acting mules.'

I seem to know that man. He was a volunteer, but he would not enlist until conscription came in, because of some precious doctrine he had about younger men without families. When he did join his first act was to ask to speak to the colonel. He was aggrieved because army doctors would not act, when he desired it, except as such. When anyone checked him he felt an ardent thirst to 'explain,' and the explanation was always that he who had checked was wrong. In the field he kept a diary and sternly would he note on its recording page that tea one day—nay, on more than one—was served 'very late indeed.' Heinous!

The continued existence of war is precarious. More than the League of Nations menaces its future. For it depends, at the last, on the infrequency of 'proper lawyers.' Armies can now be made, and moved about when made, only because the plain man who keeps the world going round does not stick up for the last ounce of his rights, or stick out for the joys of having the last word, so dourly as these. Even to keep up a game with so modest an element of voluntaryism about it as penal justice you have to have some little effort of co-operation all round. If your convicts will not even eat the whole thing begins crumbling. The 'suffragettes' showed us that. A pioneer still earlier, an Indian coolie, proved it in a Fijian gaol. Were every soldier like this diarist war would have to be dropped, not because men were too good, but because they were too prickly.

43

(II)

And yet the book told something which no other book has yet
succeeded in telling you. Wordy, cantankerous, dull, repeating
itself like a decimal, padded with cheap political 'thoughts'
gathered from old 'stunts' in bad papers—still, it came nearer than
any other to showing you the way trench warfare struck a mind
and soul quite commonplace in everything except a double dose
of native sourness. Here was nothing of M. Barbusse's doctrinaire fire to make the author pervert or exaggerate. No thrill of
drastic passion, not even the passionate self-pity of Dickens
describing his childhood as Copperfield's, stirred the plodding and
crabbed narrative. The writer seemed too peevish to be at the
pains to beautify or exalt. And so his account of the bungled
attack in which he took part is extraordinarily true to all that the
commonplace man found to be left in almost any attack when
once all the picturesque fluff filling the current literary pictures
of it was found not to be there—the touch of bathos; the supposed heroic moment only seeming a bit of a 'dud,' a miscarriage;
the hugger-mugger element of confusion; the baffling way that
the real thing did not so often give men obvious gallant things to
do as irritating puzzles to solve, muddles to liquidate at short
notice; the queer flashes of revelation, in contact with individual
enemies, of the bottomless falsity of the cheaper kind of current
war psychology.

Advances, however, were far from being the staple of warfare.
They caused the most losses, but still they did less than the years
of less sensational routine to make what changes were made by
the war in the minds of the men in the ranks. And here our
pettish author found the congenial theme for his own acrid,
accurate method. His trivial reiterations succeed, in the end, in
piling up in the reader's mind an image of that old trench life as
the sum of innumerable dreary units of irksome fatigue. This was
the normal life of the infantry private in France. For N.C.O.'s it
was lightened by the immunity of their rank from fatigue work
in the technical sense. For the officer it was much further
lightened by better quarters and the servant system. For most
of his time the average private was tired. Fairly often he was so

tired as no man at home ever is in the common run of his work.

If a company's trench strength was low and sentry-posts abounded more than usual in its sector a man might, for eight days running, get no more than one hour off duty at any one time, day or night. If enemy guns were active many of these hours off guard duty might have to be spent on trench repair. After one of these bad times in trenches a company or platoon would sometimes come out on to the road behind the communication trench like a flock of over-driven sheep. The weakest ones would fall out and drop here and there along the road, not as a rule fainting, but in the state of a horse dead-beat, to whom any amount of thrashing seems preferable to going on. Men would come out light-headed with fatigue, and ramble away to the men next to them about some great time which they had had, or meant to have, at home. Or a man would march all right till the road fetched a bend, and then he would march straight on into a ditch in his sleep. Upon a greasy road with a heavy camber I have seen a used-up man get the illusion, on a night-march back to billets, that he was walking on a round, smooth, horizontal pole or convex plank above some fearsome sort of gulf. He would struggle hard to recover imaginary losses of footing, pant and sweat and scrape desperately sideways with his feet like a frightened young horse new to harness when it leans in against the pole, with its feet skidding outwards on the setts. Down he would go, time after time, in the mud, each time as unable to rise of himself, under the weight of his pack and equipment, as any mediæval knight unhorsed and held down by the weight of his armour. Hauled up again to his feet, to be driven along like one of the spent cab-horses in Naples just strong enough to move when up, but not to rise, he would in another five minutes be agonizing again on the greasy pole of his delirium.

The querulist of the book took it hard, I remember, that more kind words did not come to the men. He saw his own lot very clearly, but not so clearly the lot of those other unfortunates who had to put the job through. A man who finds himself in charge of a spent horse at night, in a place where there may be no safe waiting till dawn, must do something. Ten to one he will flog or kick the horse into moving. He may feel that he, not the horse, is the beast; but still he will do it. So, too, will he bully and curse exhausted men into safety. That was what happened. Every decent N.C.O. and company officer—and far the larger part were decent—did what they could to humour and 'buck' the bad cases through the pangs of endurance. Some would reach the journey's end carrying whole faggots of rifles. Some would put by their own daily rations of rum to ginger beaten men through the last mile. But there would come times when only hard driving seemed to be left. *Bella, horrida bella!*

(III)

Suppose those first eight days in the front and support trenches to be the beginning of a divisional tour of sixteen days' duty in the line. For four days now the weary men would be in reserve, under enemy fire, but not in trenches; probably in the cellars of ruined houses. But these were not times of rest. Each day or night every man would make one or more journeys back to the trenches that they had left carrying some load of food, water, or munitions up to the three companies in trenches, or perhaps leading a pack-mule over land to some point near the front line, under cover of night. Even to lead a laden mule in the dark over waste ground confusingly wired and trenched is work; to get him back on to his feet when fallen and wriggling, in wild consternation, among a tangle of old barbed wire may be quite hard work.

In intervals between these journeys most men would lie in the straw in the cellars or hobble weakly about the outside of the premises, looking as boys sometimes do when stiff with many hearty hacks sustained in a hard game of football, with a chill after it. They crawled in and out of their billets like late autumn bees, feebly scraping the eight days' plating of mud off their clothes and cleaning their jack-knives after meals with the languor of the elders in the Bible to whom the grasshopper was a burden. A few robust spirits, armed with craft and subtlety more fully than the rest, would strike out, whenever released, for some 'just-a-minute,' or *estaminet*, not too far off, nor yet too near, and there lies *perdus*, lest the Company Orderly Sergeant warn them for some new liturgy. This defensive policy did not lighten the work of their brethren.

After four days of their labours as sumpter mules, or muleteers, the company would plod back for another four days of duty in trenches, come out yet more universally tired at their end, and drift back to rest-billets, out of ordinary shell-fire, for their sixteen days or so of 'divisional rest.' Here their work was really lighter, but still it was work and not rest. It did not wholly wind up in most of the men the spring that had run down while they were in the line. And then the division would go again into the line, and the old cycle be worked through once more. So most of the privates were tired the whole of the time; sometimes to the point of torment, sometimes much less, but always more or less tired.

Many, of course, lost health and drifted 'down the line,' as it was called, to the base, where work might be light, but much of the company rather more blighting than any work to the spirit. Hither, to all the divisional base depots and into the ultimate dust-hole or sink that was called 'Base Details,' there gravitated most of the walking wreckage and wastage, physical and moral, of active warfare: convalescent, sick and wounded from hospital, men found too old or too young for trench work, broken-nerved men smuggled out of the way before disaster should come, and malingerers triumphant and chuckling, or only semi-successful, suspect, and tediously over-acting.

There was the good man fretting and raging to get back to his friends and the fight, away from this tainted backwater in which the swelling flotillas of the unfit and the unwilling were left to rot at their moorings. There was the pallid and bent London clerk, faintly disguised in khaki but too blind to fight, now working furiously fifteen hours each day of his seven-day week in the orderly-room—no Sunday here, no Saturday afternoon— for pure love of international right. There was the dug-out, the Grenadier Guards sergeant major of sixty, the handsome and melancholy old boy, a Victorian survivor into our little vulgar age, with a careful and dignified manner and mighty memories of a radiant past in London, when all parades, for a good-conduct-man well up in his drill, were over by half-past ten in the morning and he had a permanent midnight pass into barracks and so could act as a super at one of the theatres every night except when doing a guard, and see life and move among genius and beauty, making good money. Oh, yes, he had acted with Irving and Booth, and lived the life, and heard the chimes at midnight.

But also the veteran crooks, old dregs of the Regular Army, Queen Victoria's worst bargains, N.C.O.'s who would boast that they had not been once on parade in the last twenty years, waiters and caterers for the whole of their martial careers till the liquor fairly lipped over the edge of their eyelids and bleached the blue of their eyes. You would hear one of them boast that no doctor on earth could find him out to be fit when he, the tactician, wished otherwise. Another had made pathological studies, learning up the few conjectural symptoms of maladies that show no outward trace; as science advanced to the point of recording detectively the true state of the heart he had deftly changed ground, relinquished rheumatism of that organ and done some work of research into pains in the head; much faith did he put, too, in the sciatic nerve. When a couple of these savants slept in one tent they would argue after Lights Out—was sciatica safest, or shell-shock, or general debility? 'Them grey hairs should be a lot of use to you, corp.,' one of them would quite feelingly say to a new man in the tent, 'when you want to get swinging the lead.'

While these ignoble presences befouled the air of a base, good things, also, were there; but you seldom quite knew which was which. All very well for the King to come out with his 'Go, hang yourself, brave Crillon! We fought at Arques and you were not there.' But if you, too, were not at the battle—if some un-lucky effect of combustion compelled you to live as a messmate of Crillon, far, far from Arques when the battle was on, you would have to use tact. Somehow the man who was undisguisedly keen to get back to the centre of things felt a slight coldness per-vading the air about him. It was as if a workman, who might have so easily let well alone, had sinned against the trade-union spirit, helped to raise the standard of employers' expectation, forced the pace of dutifulness in a world where authority could be trusted to speed things up quite enough. Even officers tended to deprecate the higher temperatures of ardour in other ranks of base establishments. 'You're out for distinction,'—one honest rationalist would advise—'that's what it is. Well, trust to me—up the line's not the place where you get it. Every time a war ends you'll find most of the decorations go to the people at G.H.Q., L. of C., and the bases. So, if you want a nice row of ribbons to show to your kiddies, stop here.' And another would put it more subtly: 'Isn't one's duty, as a rule, just here and now?' Some were good-natured; they were not for keeping the primrose path all to themselves. Others were anxious lest the taking of steep and thorny paths, as they thought them, should come to be 'the done thing.'

(v)

The men who could not shirk the choice of Hercules, for other people, were the doctors. The stay of every N.C.O. or man at a base depot was on probation. Each had to go before a Medical Board soon after he came. It adjudged him either T.B. (Temporary Base) or P.B. (Permanent Base). If marked T.B. he went before the Board again once a week, and each time he might be marked T.B. again, or, if his disablement was thought graver or more likely to last, P.B.; or he might be marked A. (Active Service), and then he would join the next draft from home going up to his own battalion or another battalion of his regiment. When once a man was marked P.B. he only went before the Board once a month, and each time he, too, might be marked either P.B., T.B., or A.

Chance relegated me once for some weeks to a base and gave me the job of marching parties of crocks, total and partial, real, half-real, and sham, across the sand dunes to the place where the faculty did its endeavour to sort them. A picture remains of a hut with a long table in it: two middle-aged army doctors sitting beyond it, like dons at a Viva, and each of my party in turn taking his stand at attention, my side of the table, facing the Board, like so many Oliver Twists. The presiding officer takes a manifest pride in knowing all the guile and subtlety of soldier-men. No taking *him* in—that is proclaimed in every look and tone. He has had several other parties before him to-day, and the lamp of his faith, never dazzling while these rites are on, has burnt low.

'Well, my man—cold feet, I suppose?' he begins, to the first of my lamentable party. As some practitioners are said to begin all treatment with a prefatory purge, so would this psychologist start with a good full dose of insult and watch the patient's reaction under the stimulus.

'No, sir, me 'eart's thrutched up,' says the examinee. Then, while the Board perforates him from head to foot for some seconds with a basilisk stare of unbelief, he dribbles out at intervals, in a voice that bespeaks falling hope, such ineffective addenda as 'Can't get me sleep' and 'Not a smile in me.'

'Very picturesque, indeed,' says the senior expert in doubting. 'We'll see to that "thrutched" heart of yours. Kardiagraph case. Next man.'

The suspect, duly spat upon, slinks out. The next man takes his place at the table. The president gives him the Dogberry eye that means: 'Masters, it is proved already that you are little better than false knaves; and it will go near to be thought so shortly.' What he says is: 'Another old hospital bird? Eh? Now, hadn't you better get back to work before you're in trouble?'

The target of this consputation is almost convinced by its force that he must be guilty of something, if only he knew what it was. Still, he repeats authority's last diagnosis as well as he can: 'Mine's Arthuritic rheumatism, sir, An' piles.'

'Fall out and strip. Next man.' While the next is taking his stand the presiding M.O. has been making a note, and does not look up before saying 'Well, what's the matter with *you*— besides rheumatism?'

'No rheumatism, sir. And nothing else.' The voice is as stiff as it dares.

The presiding M.O. seems taken aback. Why, here is a fellow not playing up to him! Making a nasty break in the long line of cases that fed his darling cynicism so well! Flat burglary as ever was committed. The second member of the Board comes to life and begins in a tone that savours of dissatisfaction: 'Well, you're the first man——'

'I'm an N.C.O., sir.' The young lance-sergeant's voice is again about as stiff as is safe. Quite safe, though, this time. For the presiding M.O. is a Regular. Verbal points of military correctitude are the law and the prophets to him. He cannot be wholly

sorry when junior colleagues, temporary commissioners, slip up
on even the least of these shreds of orange-peel. Like Susan
Nipper, he knows his place—'me being a permanency'—and
thinks that 'temporaries' ought to know theirs. So he amends the
outsider's false start to: 'You're the first N.C.O. or man who has
come before us this morning and not said he had rheumatism.'

The sergeant, whom I have known for some days as a choleric
body, holds his tongue, having special reasons just now not to risk
a court-martial. 'Well,' the president snaps as if in resentment of
this self-control, 'what *is* the matter with you?'

'Fit as can be, sir.'

'What are you doing down here, then, away from your unit?'

'Obeying orders of Medical Board, sir. No. 8 General Hospital,
December 8.'

'Not sorry, either, I daresay,' the president mutters, wobbling
back towards his first line of approach to the business. 'Not very
keen to go back up the line, sergeant, eh?'

'It's all I want, sir, thank you.' The sergeant puts powerful
brakes on his tongue and says only that. But he has sadly disconcerted the faculty. A major with twenty years' service has cast
himself for the fine sombre part of recording angel to note all the
cowardice and mendacity that he can. And here is a minor actor
forgetting his part and putting everything out. From where I am
keeping a wooden face near the door I see opposition arising in
the heart of the outraged psychologist beyond the table.

A sound professional instinct reinforces the personal one.
Whenever a soldier goes before a Medical Board it is soon clear
that he wants to be thought either less fit than he is or more fit.
The doctor's first impulse, as soon as he sees which way the man's
wishes tend, is to lean towards the other. And this, in due
measure, is just. We all understate or overstate symptoms to our
own family doctors according to what we fear or desire. The
doctor rightly tries to detect the disturbing force in the patient's
mind, and to discount for it duly—just like 'laying-off' for a side
wind in shooting. So now the president sees light again. The
Board is now out to find the lance-sergeant a crock. 'Hold
out your wrists,' says the senior member. The pulse is jealously
felt.

'Rotten!' the senior member says to the junior. Then, penetratingly, to the sergeant: 'What's that cicatrice you've got on the back of your hand? Both hands! Show me here.'

Two spongy, purplish-red pads of new flesh are inspected. 'Burns, scarcely healed!' says the president wrathfully. 'Skin just the strength of wet tissue-paper! Man-alive, you've a bracelet of ulcers all round your wrists. Never wash, eh?' When liquid fire flayed a man's hands to the sleeve, but not further, the skin was apt to break out, as he recovered, in small, deep boils about the frontier of the new skin and the old. The sergeant does not answer. He wants no capital punishment under the Army Act.

'Man's an absolute wreck,' says the major. 'Debility, wounds imperfectly healed, blood-poisoning likely. Not fit for the line for two months to come. P.B.—eh!' he turns to his junior.

'That's what *I* should say, sir,' the junior concurs, in a tone of desperate independence.

'Next man,' says the major. Before the lance-sergeant has quite stalked to the door the major calls after him 'Sergeant!'

'Sir?' says the sergeant, furious and red but contained.

'You're a damned good man, but it won't do,' says the major. 'Good luck to you!' Great are the forces of decent human relentment after a hearty let-out with the temper.

The inquisition proceeds, still on that Baconian principle of finding out which is a man's special bent and then bending the twig pretty hard in the other direction; still, too, with the dry light of reason a little suffused, as Bacon would say, with the humours of the affections, of vanity, ill-temper and impatience. Nearly everybody is morally weary. Most of the men inspected have outlived the first profuse impulse to court more of bodily risk than authority expressly orders. Most of the doctors, living here in the distant rear of the war, have outlived their first generous belief in an almost universally high *moral* among the men. In the training-camps in 1914 the safe working presumption about any unknown man was that he only wanted to get at the enemy as soon as he could. Now the working presumption, the starting hypothesis, is that a man wants to stay in, out of the rain, as long as you let him. Faith has fallen lame; generosity flags; there has entered into the soul as well as the body the malady known to athletes as staleness.

(VI)

The war had more obvious disagreeables, too; you have heard all
about them: the quelling coldness of frosty nights spent in
soaked clothes—for no blankets were brought up to the trenches;
the ubiquitous dust and stench of corpses and buzzing of millions
of corpse-fed flies on summer battlefields; and so on, and so on—
no need to go over the list. But these annoyances seemed to me
to do less in the way of moulding the men's cast of mind than
that general, chronic weariness, different from all the common
fatigues of peace, inasmuch as each instalment of this course of
exhaustion was not sandwiched in between heavenly contrasts of
utter rest before and after—divine sleeps in a bed and dry clothes,
and meals on a table, with a white tablecloth on it and shiny
glasses. It raised some serious thoughts in professional football-
players and boxers who had believed they were strong, and in
navvies and tough mountaineers. You need to know this in order
to understand the redoubled ardour with which that capital
soldier, the Lancashire miner, has sought the off-day and ensued
it since he came back from campaigning abroad.

    You need, too, to know it in order to chart out the general
post-war condition of mind with its symptoms of apathy, callousness, and lassitude. Something has got to come of it if you have
lain for a time in the garden of Proserpine, where the great values
decline and faith and high impulse fall in like *soufflés* grown tepid,
and fatalistic indifference comes out of long flat expanses of tiring
sameness.

> *I am tired of tears and laughter,*
> *And men that laugh and weep;*
> *Of what may come hereafter*
> *For men that sow to reap:*
> *I am weary of days and hours,*
> *Blown buds of barren flowers,*
> *Desires and dreams and powers*
> *And everything but sleep.*
>
> *From too much love of living,*
> *From hope and fear set free,*

We thank with brief thanksgiving,
Whatever gods may be,
That no life lives for ever;
That dead men rise up never;
That even the weariest river
Winds somewhere safe to sea.

Heaven forbid that I should impute any melodious Swinburn-
ian melancholy, or any other form of luxurious self-pity, to
millions of good fellows still fighting the good fight against
circumstance. They would hoot at the notion. But in nearly all
of them hope has, at some time or other, lost her first innocence.
Time and place came when the spirit, although unbroken, went
numb: the dull mind came to feel as if its business with ardour
and choric spheres and quests of Holy Grails, and everything but
rest, had been done quite a long while ago. Well chained to an
oar in the galley, closely kept to a job in the mine, men caught
a touch of the recklessness of the slave—if the world were so foul,
let it go where it chose; they would snatch what they could,
when they could; drink, and let the world go round.

It is not sense to hope to reattain at will that deflowered
virginity of faith. Others who have it may come in good time
to be a majority of us all. Already three yearly 'classes' of men
who did not suffer that immense loss of experience which came
with war service have come of age since the war; the new skin
grows over the wounds. But we cannot write off a mere dream,
with no after effects, the time when it was a kind of trench fashion
to meet the demoded oaths of a friend with the dogma that 'There
is no —— God .'

Chapter V

THE SHEEP THAT WERE NOT FED

(1)

'OF late years,' the novel of *Shirley* begins, 'an abundant shower of curates has fallen upon the North of England; they lie very thick on the hills; every parish has one or more of them; they are young enough to be very active, and ought to be doing a great deal of good.' This blessing, conferred on the West Riding a little before Waterloo, descended on our Western Front a little after the first battle of the Marne.

It was received by our troops with the greater thanksgiving because it brought with it no perceptible revival of church parades, a ministration of which the average private, *l'homme moyen sensuel* of Matthew Arnold, had taken a long and glad farewell on leaving Salisbury Plain. Like the infinite cleaning of brass-work, the hearing of many well-meaning divines in the Tidworth garrison church had been one of the tribulations through which the defender of Britain must work out his passage to France. With the final order to tarnish his buttons with fire and oil there came also a longed-for release from regular Sunday adjurations to keep sober and think of his end. 'The Lorrd,' said a grim Scots corporal, a hanging judge of a sermon, after hearing the last essay of our English Bossuets before he went to the wars, 'hath turrned the capteevity of Zion.' No more attendance for him at such 'shauchlin' ' athletic displays as the wrestlings of the southron divinity passman with the lithe and sinuous mind of St Paul. 'Sunday,' the blithe Highlander in *Waverley* said, 'seldom cam aboon the pass of Bally Brough.' For better or worse, as a reliever from work or a restrainer of play, Sunday seldom came across the Channel during the war. A man in the ranks might be six months in France and not find a religious service of any kind coming his way, whether he dreaded or sought it.

Yet chaplains abounded. Not measures, but men, to invert the old phrase. And men of all kinds, as might safely be guessed.

55

There was the hero and saint, T. B. Hardy, to whom a consuming
passion of human brotherhood brought, as well as rarer things,
the M.C., the D.S.O., the V.C., the unaccepted invitation of the
King, when he saw Hardy in France, to come home as one of his
own chaplains and live, and then the death which everyone had
seen to be certain. There was a chaplain drunk at dinner in
Gobert's restaurant at Amiens on the evening of one of the
bloodiest days of the first battle of the Somme. There was the
circumspect ecclesiastical statesman, out to see that in this grand
shaking-up and rearranging of pre-war positions and values the
right cause—whichever of the right causes was his—was not jilted
or any way wronged. There was the man who, urged by national
comradeship, would have been a soldier but that his bishop barred
it; to be an army chaplain was the next best thing. There was the
man who, urged by a different instinct, felt irresistibly, as many
laymen did, that at the moment the war was the central thing
in the whole world, and that it was unbearable not to be at the
centre of things. And there was, in great force, the large, healthy,
pleasant young curate not severely importuned by a vocation, the
ex-athlete, the prop and stay of village cricket-clubs, the good
fellow whom the desires of parents, the gaiety of his youth at
the university, and the whole drift of things about him had
shepherded unresistingly into the open door of the Church.
Sudden, unhoped-for, the war had brought him the chance of
escape back to an almost solely physical life, like his own happy
youth of rude health, only better: a life all salt and tingling with
vicissitudes of simple bodily discomfort and pleasure, fatigue and
rest, risk and the ceasing of risk; a heaven after the flatness, the
tedium, the cloying security and the confounded moral problems
attending the uninspired practice of professional brightness and
breeziness in an uncritical parish. He abounded so much that
whenever now one hears the words 'army chaplain' his large,
genial image springs up of itself in the mind.

(II)

In the eyes of the men he had notable merits. He was a running
fountain, more often than not, of good cigarettes. Of the exceed-
ing smallness of Low Country beer he could talk, man to man,

with knowledge and right feeling. He gladly frequented the least healthy parts of the line, and would frankly mourn the pedantry which denied him a service revolver and did not even allow him the grievous ball-headed club with which a mediæval bishop felt himself free to take his own part in a war, because with this lethal tool he did not exactly shed blood, though he dealt liberally enough in contused wounds that would serve equally well. Having a caste of his own, not precisely the combatant officer's, he had a tongue less rigidly tied in the men's hearing, so he could soothe the couch of a wounded sergeant by telling him, with a diverting gusto, how downily the old colonel, the one last un-gummed, had timed his enteric inoculation at home so as to rescue himself from the fiery ordeal of a divisional field-day. These were solid merits. And yet there was something about this type of chaplain—he had his counterpart in all the churches—with which the common men-at-arms would privily and temperately find a little fault. He seemed to be only too much afraid of having it thought that he was anything more than one of themselves. He had, with a vengeance, 'no clerical nonsense about him.' The vigour with which he threw off the parson and put on the man and the brother did not always strike the original men and brothers as it was intended. Your virilist chaplain was apt to overdo, to their mind, his jolly implied disclaimers of any com-promising connection with kingdoms not of this world. For one thing, he was, for the taste of people versed in carnage, a shade too fussily bloodthirsty. Nobody made such a point of aping your little trench affectations of callousness; nobody else was so anxious to keep you assured that the blood of the enemy smelt as good to his nose as it could to any of yours. In the whole blood-and-iron province of talk he would not only outshine any actual combatant—that is quite easy to do—but he would outshine any colonel who lived at a base. I never met a regimental officer or 'other rank' who wanted a day more of the war for himself, his friends, or his country after the Armistice. But I have heard more than one chaplain repining because the killing was not to go on until a few German towns had been smashed and our last thing in gas had had a fair innings.

No doubt the notion was good, in a way. If the parson in war was to make the men mind what he said he must not stand too coldly aloof from 'the men's point of view': he must lay his mind close up alongside theirs, so as to get a hold of their souls. It sounds all right; the wisdom of the serpent has been bidden to back up the labours of the dove. And yet the men, however nice they might be to the chaplain himself, would presently say to each other in private that 'Charlie came it too thick,' while still allowing that he was a 'proper good sort.' They felt there was something or other—they could not tell what—which he might have been and which he was not. They could talk lyddite and ammonal well enough for themselves, but, surprising to say, they secretly wanted a change from themselves; had the parsons really nothing to say of their own about this noisome mess in which the good old world seemed to be foundering? The relatively heathen English were only groping about to find out what it was that they missed; the Scots, who have always had theology for a national hobby, made nearer approaches to being articulate. Part of a famous division of Highland infantry were given one day, as a special treat, a harangue by one of the most highly reputed of chaplains. This spell-binder preached like a tempest—the old war-sermon, all God of Hosts and chariots of wrath and laying His rod on the back of His foes, and other thunderous sounds such as were then reverberating, no doubt, throughout the best churches in Berlin. In the south-western postal district of London, too, this cyclone might have had a distinguished success at the time. As soon as the rumbling died away one of the hard-bitten kilted sergeants leant across to another and quoted dourly: 'A great and strong wind, but the Lorrd was not in the wind.'

(III)

'I've been a Christian all my life, but this war is a bit too serious.' So saying, a certain New Army recruit had folded up his religion in 1914 and put it away, as it were, in a drawer with his other civil attire to wait until public affairs should again permit of their use. He had said it quite simply. A typical working-class Englishman, literal, serious, and straight, he had not got one loop of subtlety or one vibration of irony in his whole mind. Like most of his kind he had, as a rule, left church-going to others. Like

most of them, too, he had read the Gospels and found that whatever Christ had said mattered enormously: it built itself into the
mind; when any big choice had to be made it was at least a part
of that which decided. Not having ever been taught how to
dodge an awkward home-thrust at his conscience, he felt, all un-
blunted, the point of what Christ had said about such things as
wealth and war and loving one's enemies. Getting rich made you
bad; fighting was evil—better submit than resist. There was no
getting over such doctrine, nor round it: why try?

Ever since those disconcerting bombs were originally thrown
courageous divines and laymen have been rushing in to pick
them up and throw them away, combining as well as they could
an air of respect for the thrower with tender care for the mental
ease of congregations occupied generally in making money and
occasionally in making war. Yet there they lie, miraculously
permanent and disturbing, as if just thrown. Now and then one
will go off, with seismic results, in the mind of some St Francis
or Tolstoy. And yet it remains where it was, like the plucked
Golden Bough: *uno avulso, non deficit alter*, ready as ever to
work on a guileless mind like our friend's.

But this war had to be won; that was flat. It was like putting
out houses on fire, or not letting children be killed; it did not
even need to be proved; that we had got to win was now the one
quite certain thing left in a world of shaken certainties. Any
religion or anything else that seemed to chill, or deter, or suggest
an alternative need not be wholly renounced. But it had to be put
away in a drawer. After the war, when that dangerous precept
about the left cheek could no longer do serious harm, it might
come out again; our friend would see what could be done. For
he was a man more strongly disposed than most of his fellows to
hold, if he honestly could, the tenets of some formal religion.
'They got hold o' something,' he used to say, with curiosity and
some respect, of more regular practitioners than himself. 'Look
at the Salvation Army legging along in the mud and their eyes
fair shining with happiness! Aye, they got on to *something*.' He
would investigate, when the time came.

The testimonies that might have ensued were fore-closed by a
shell that buried him alive in Oppy Wood, under the Vimy
Ridge, where he was engaged in diverting the energies of the
Central Powers from the prostrate army of Nivelle. He had by
then been two years in France, and had told a few friends about
various 'queer feels' and 'rum goes' which he would not have
known by name if you had called them spiritual experiences. One
of his points—though he did not put it in that way—was that in
war a lot of raw material for making some sort of religion was
lying about, but that war also made some of the finished doctrinal
products now extant look pretty poor, especially, as he said, 'all
the damning department.' Rightly or wrongly, no men who have
been close friends for a year, and who know that in the next few
hours they are nearly as likely as not to be killed together in
doing what they all hold to be right, will entertain on any terms
the idea of any closing of gates of divine mercy, open to themselves, in the face of any comrade in the business.

The sunshine of one of the first clement days of 1916 drew
him about as far as I heard him go on the positive side. 'You
know what it is,' he said in the course of one of the endless trench
talks, 'when you got to make up your mind to do as you oughter.
Worry and fuss, and oh, ain't it too hard, and why the 'ell can't
I let myself off!—that's how it is. Folla me?'

The audience grunted assent. 'Some other time,' he pursued,
'perhaps once in ten years, it's all t'other way. You're set free
like. Kind of a miracle. Don't even have to think what you're
going to get by it. All you know is that there's just the one thing,
in all the whole world, good enough. Doing it ain't even hard.
All the sport there ever was has been took out of everything else
and put into that. Kind of a miracle. Folla me?'

'That's right,' another man confirmed. 'You'll see it at fires
when people are like to be burnt. Men'll go fair mad to help
them. Don't think. Don't feel it if they're hurt. Fair off it to get
at them—same as a dog when you throw a stick in a pond.'

'Ah, then,' contributed somebody else, 'you've only to hear a
man with a grand tenor voice in a song till you'll feel a coolness

blowing softly and swif'ly over your face and then gone, the way you'd have died on a cross with all the pleasure in life while it lasted.'

'Aye, and you'll get it from whisky,' another put in. 'Isn't it just what more men'll get drunk for than anything else? And why the rum's double before you go over?'

No doubt you know all about it from books, and you may prefer the wording of that tentative approach made by the most spiritually-minded of modern philosophers to a definition of God—'Something that is in and about me, in the consciousness of which I am free from fear and desire—something which would make it easy to do the most (otherwise) difficult thing without any other motive except that it was the one thing worth doing.' And William James has, of course, shown more skill in explaining what mystic ecstasy is and what is its place in religion, and what its relations to such mirages of itself as the mock inspirations of Antony's lust and Burns' drunkenness.

And yet the clumsy fumblings of uninstructed people among things of the spirit might, one imagines, be just such stuff as a skilled teacher and leader in this field might have delighted to come upon and to inspirit and marshal. With tongues unwontedly loosened men would set to and dig out of themselves, not knowing what it was, the clay of which the bricks are made with which religions are built. One man, with infinite exertions of disentanglement, would struggle up to some expression of the fugitive trance of realization into which he had found he could throw himself by letting his mind go, for all it was worth, on the thought of his own self, his 'I-ness,' until for some few seconds of poised exaltation he had thought self clean away and was free. 'It first came by a fluke when I was a kiddy. If I'd lie in my cot, very still, and look hard a long time at the candle, and think very hard—'I,' 'I,' 'I,' what's 'I'? I could work myself up to that state I'd be right outside o' myself, and seeing the queer little body I'd been, with my thought about 'I' doing this and 'I' getting that, and the way that I'd thought it was natural I should, and no such a thing as any 'I' there all the time, or only one to the whole set of us. Hard I'd try, every time, to hold the thing on. Seemed as if there was no end to what I might get to know if I could make it last out, that sort of rum start. But the thing went to bits every

time, next moment after I'd got it worked up, and there I'd be left
on the mat like, and thinking 'Gosh! what a pitch I got up to
that time!' and how I'd screw it up higher, next go.'

Then somebody else would bring up the way he had been
taken by that queer little rent in the veil of common experience
—the sudden rush of certainty that something which is happen-
ing now has all happened before, or that some place, when first
we see it, has really been known to us of old and is only being
revisited now, not discovered. You know how you seem, when
that sudden light comes, to escape for a while from your common thoughts about time, as if out of a prison in which you have
been shut up so long that you had almost forgotten what it is to
be free: it flashes into your mind that immortality, for all you
know, may exist within one moment; that life, for all you know,
may draw out into state after state, and that all that you are
conscious of at common times might be merely a drop or two
lipping over the edge of the full vessel of some vast consciousness
animating the whole world.

Another man would bring into the common stock a recollection of the kind of poignant portrait dream that sometimes
comes: not a dream of any incident, but only the face of a
friend, more living than life, with all the secret kindness and
loneliness of his mind suddenly visible in the face, so that you
think of him as you think of your mother when she is dead and
the stabbing insight of remorse begins.

Thus would these inexpert people hang unconsciously about
the uncrossed threshold of religion. With minds which had
recovered in some degree the penetrative simplicity of a child's,
they disinterred this or that unidentified bone of the buried God
from under the monumental piles of débris which the learned, the
cunning, and the proud, priests and kings, churches and chapels,
had heaped up over the ideas of perfect love, of faith that would
leave all to follow that love, and of the faithful spirit's release
from mean fears of extinction. In talk they could bring each
other up to the point of feeling that little rifts had opened here
and there in the screens which are hung round the life of man
on the earth, and that they had peeped through into some large
outer world that was strange only because they were used to a
small and dim one. They were prepared and expectant. If any

official religion could ever refine the gold out of all that rich alluvial drift of 'obstinate questionings of sense and outward things,' now was its time. No figure of speech, among all these that I have mixed, can give the measure of the greatness of that opportunity.

(V)

Nobody used it: the tide in the affairs of churches flowed its best, but no church came to take it. Instead, as if chance had planned a kind of satiric practical epigram, came the brigade chaplain. As soon as his genial bulk hove in sight, and his cheery robustious chaff began blowing about, the shy and uncouth muse of our savage theology unfolded her wings and flew away. Once more the talk was all footer and rations and scragging the Kaiser, and how 'the Hun' would walk a bit lame after the last knock he had got. Very nice, too, in its way. And yet there had been a kind of a savour about the themes that had now shambled back in confusion, before the clerical onset, into their twilight lairs in the souls of individual laymen.

When you want to catch the Thames gudgeon you first comb the river's bed hard with a long rake. In the turbid water thus caused the creatures will be on the feed, and if you know how to fish you may get a great take. For our professional fishers of men in the army the war did the raking *gratis*. The men came under their hands at the time of most drastic experience in most of the men's lives, immersed in a new and strange life of sensations at once simple and intense, shaken roughly out of the world of mechanical habit which at most times puts a kind of bar between one's mind and truth, living always among swiftly dying friends and knowing their own death at any time to be as probable as anyone's. To get rid of your phlegm, it was said, is to be a philosopher. It is also to be a saint, at least in the rough; you have broken the frozen ground; you can grow anything now; you can see the greatest things in the very smallest, so that sunrise on Inverness Copse is the morning of the first day and a spoonful of rum and a biscuit a sacrament. Imagine the religious revival that there might have been if some man of apostolic genius had had the fishing in the troubled water, the ploughing and sowing of the broken soil.

The frozen fountain would have leapt,
The buds gone on to blow,
The warm south wind would have awaked
To melt the snow.

Nothing now perceptible came of it all. What, indeed, could the average army chaplain have done, with his little budget of nice traits and limitations? How had we ever armed and equipped him? When you are given an infant earth to fashion out of a whirling ball of flaming metals and gases, then good humour, some taste for adventure, distinction at cricket, a jolly way with the men, and an imperfect digestion of thirty-nine partly masticated articles may not carry you far. You may come off, by no fault of your own, like the curate in Shakespeare who was put up to play Alexander the Great: 'A marvellous good neighbour, i' faith, and a very good bowler: but, for Alisander—alas, you see how 'tis—a little o'erparted.'

The men, once again, did not put it in that way. They did not miss anything that most of them could have described. They only felt a vacancy, an unspecified void, like the want of some unknown great thing in their generals' minds and in the characters of their rulers at home. The chaplain's tobacco was all to the good; so was the civil tongue that he kept in his head; so were all the good turns that he did. But, when it came to religion, were these things 'all there was to it'? Had the churches really not 'got hold of something,' with all their enormous deposits of stone and mortar and clerical consequence? So, in his own way, the army chaplain, too, became a tributary brook feeding the general reservoir of disappointment and mistrust that was steadily filled by the surface drainage of all the higher ground of our British social landscape under the dirty weather of the war.

Chapter VI

'WARE POLITICIANS

(I)

WHEN a man enlisted during the war he found himself living the life of the common man in a Communist State. Once inside he had no more choices to make than a Russian under the Soviet. His work, his pay, his food, his place and mode of living were fixed from on high. He might not even decide whether he should remain a soldier or be turned, say, into a miner. If the wisdom that sat up aloft put him down for a draft to a tunnelling company, to earth he went. He had ceased to be Economic Man, the being whom we were brought up to regard as causing the world to go round by making a bee-line to the best pay available. Now he was ex-Economic Man, or Economic Man popped off all the hooks that had fastened him into a place in the system called capitalistic by those who least admire it. No one was left to say of a job any longer that you might 'take it or leave it,' for leaving was barred. You could not be called a wage-slave, for you got no wages to speak of. You had become a true 'proletarian' under a pretty big-fisted dictatorship. It might not be a dictatorship of the proletariat, but a dictatorship smells about as sweet by one name as another when it levers you out of bed before dawn or ties you up to the wheel of a gun for cutting a job that irks you. Dr Johnson declined to attempt to settle degrees of precedence between a flea and a louse. It is as hard to decide between the charms of a 'sanitary fatigue' when done for our War Office and when done for Mr Lenin.

In a sense, no doubt, the average man liked it all—the sense in which men like to break the ice in the Serpentine for a swim. He had willed it. He felt that when it was over it would be a good thing to have done. But he also saw, perhaps with surprise, that there were many men who liked it wholly, without any juggling with future and pluperfect tenses. They liked to have their hours of rising and going to bed settled by colonel or Soviet rather than face for themselves this distracting problem in self-government. They liked meals which they did not choose, and which might not be good, but which came up of themselves, in their season, like grass. They liked quarters which they might perhaps have to share with brethren too weak to carry their liquor and not too wise to essay great feats of the kind, but which, anyhow, did not have to be sought for, rented, furnished, and, on every Monday, paid for with a separate pang. They liked, at any rate as the lesser evil, work which was no subject of either collective or individual bargain, but came out of the sky, like the weather, usually open to objection, but sometimes not.

Perhaps you concluded, after a time, that there must be some temperaments communistic or socialistic by nature, like the 'souls Christian by nature' of the theologians. You might even have suspected that in all this wide field of dispute the most fundamental difference is not between the intrinsic and absolute merits of the individualistic and of the communistic State, but between two contrasted human types—the type which is actually happiest in communal messes and dormitories and playgrounds and forced labour and State-fixed pay in a State-chosen career, and the type which exults in even the smallest separate cottage and garden, as a lion rejoices in his own den; the type which cooks its mutton with a special rapture in an exclusive oven, however imperfect, and sallies forth rejoicing, as the bridegroom goeth out from his chamber, to angle for the dearest market for the labour of its hands and the cheapest for its victuals. So that the only ideal solution might be to cut up the world, or each of its States, into two hemispheres, as trains are divided into 'non-smoking' and 'smoking.' A little difficult, perhaps; but then it is difficult to make either breed be happy in the other's paradise.

(II)

Other speculations were apt to visit your mind if, later on in the war, as a New Army officer, you watched, open-mouthed, the way that much of the Regular Army's business was done. In civil life you might have had wild dreams of what business life would be like if its one great, black, ruling, quelling possibility were for ever removed, if the last Official Receiver had gone the way of the great auk, and the two-handed engine of bankruptcy stood no longer at the door, its place being taken by a genie carrying countless Treasury notes and ready to come in and 'make it all right' as soon as you gave the slightest rub to the electric lamp on your desk. How nobly free you would be from the base care of overhead charges! How pungently you would keep in his proper place any large customer whose tone displeased you! How handsomely, when in a generous mood, you would cast away the sordid preoccupation of getting value for money and indulge yourself with a sight of the smile-wreathed face of a friend to whom you had given the bargain of a lifetime! How dignified a leisure you would enjoy after all those years of answering letters on the day you got them! Or, if that were your line, how high you would wave the banner of an ideal precision, stooping to none of the slavish, supple complaisances of competitive commerce, but making everyone who wrote a letter to you mind his P's and Q's, and do the thing in form, and go on doing it until he got it right, as long as the forests of Scandinavia held out to supply you both with stationery!

In the throes of a great war, and within sound of its guns, the genius of our race achieved, at any rate in some minor departmental Edens, this approach to a business man's heaven. To the rightful inhabitants of these paradises the intrusion of an ordinary fallen business man, with his vulgar notions of efficiency, gave something of a shock. He seemed cold and clammy—a serpent in the garden. 'At the War Office,' an old Staff officer plaintively said to one of these kill-joys, 'we never used to open the afternoon letters till the next day.' He felt that life would lose its old-world bloom if he had to do things on the nail. 'After all, it won't kill the British taxpayer'—that was another golden formula.

(III)

Returned from these illuminating experiences the victorious soldier finds the British taxpayer—not, indeed, killed, but rubbing his wounds and groaning and being advised by several different kinds of friends to try if a hair, or perhaps the whole skin, of the dog that bit him will make him feel better. 'Put your trust,' say the august political authoritarians, 'in your natural rulers, from

Lord Chaplin and the Duke of Northumberland down to about as low as Sir Eric Geddes; scrap all the outworn and discredited humbug of democracy and parliamentarism; recognize that only a governing class with ample traditions of skill and devotion can govern to any effect.'

'Rats!' observe the Extreme Left; 'all that ramp was exposed long ago—ruling class and Parliament, and all of it. Turn down aristocracy and democracy, too, and put your money on the Dictatorship of the Proletariat and——' At which the poor tax-paying proletarian looks up with a gleam of hope and asks if he may begin dictating now. With a pitying smile the Extreme Left explains that it is to be named his dictatorship, but that it will be exercised not by him but by the Proper Persons. Will he elect them? he asks. Oh, no; that would be mere *bourgeois* Liberalism, quite out of date. Well, he asks, how is he to feel sure that they will do what he wants? Can he doubt it?—he is reproachfully asked. Does he not see that men ruling only as dictators for the whole nation, men serving only their country and no grubby individual employer or caucus, will and must be fired, at once and for ever, with a new spirit of devotion, wisdom, purity, human-ity, and love such as was never yet seen on earth—indeed, could not be seen on it while its surface was defaced with Houses of Parliament and joint-stock mills?

At this point the demobilized business man is likely to go out sorrowfully, reflecting that thanks to the war he has known, in turn, what it is to be one of the rulers, and what it is to be one of the ruled, in a community where the people below have no hold on the people above, and where the people above are pricked by no coarser spur than their own pure zeal for the best of causes in the sorest of its straits. Communism delights him not, nor Toryism either.

Nor, indeed, any other political creed of all those that he knows. Liberals he has, perhaps, come to figure as sombre and dry, all-round prohibitors, humanitarians but not humanists, people with democratic principles but not democratic sympathies, uncomradelike lovers of man, preaching the brotherhood of nations but not knowing how to speak without offence to a workman from their own village. The Labour Party, indeed, he may feel to be, as yet, not wholly damned, but chiefly because it has never been tried at the big job. Its leaders have not, like the Liberal and Conservative chiefs, to answer for any grand public triumphs of incapacity like the diplomacy that gave Bulgaria and Turkey to Germany. Labour has not the name of Gallipoli to wear on its party colours; the *Goeben* and the *Breslau* did not escape with it at the Admiralty; none of its leaders intrigued with any general against his superiors; it did not turn Ireland's offered help into enmity in the hour of need. What of that, though? Liberals and Conservatives, too, might not have failed yet if they had not been tested. As likely as not that the Labour chiefs, too, would show, at a pinch, the old vice of the others—live and act in a visionary world of their own, the world as they would have liked to have it, not the world in which rough work and fighting and starving go on and the people who make it go round are not politicians.

(IV)

A century of almost unbroken European peace—unbroken, that is, by wars hugely destructive—had built up insensibly in men's minds a consciousness of an unbounded general stability in the political as well as in the physical world. The crust of the political globe seemed to have caked, on the whole, almost as hard and cool as that of the elderly earth. It felt as if it were so firm that we could safely play the fool on it, as boys jump on the ice of a pond and defy it to break under them. So an immense tolerance of political rubbish had grown up. On decade after decade of indulgence the man of booming phrases and grandiosely noble professions had swelled into a marvel of inflation surpassing any barking frog at the Zoo. That doing of hard and plain work well, which is the basis of all right living and success in men or nations, had grown almost dull in the sight of a people who took too seriously the trumpetings and naggings of the various fashionable schools of virtuosi in political blatancy. It would not be common sense to suppose that no psychological change of any moment would, in any case, have been wrought by a passage from that substantially stable world into a world in which the three great empires of Continental Europe have been ground to dust like Ypres. Anyhow, the adventure of finding our cooled and solid earth turning once more into a ball of fire under the foot would not have left the state of our minds quite as it had been. They are all the more changed now that most of us feel we have pulled through the scrape, scorched and battered, by our own sweat, and not by the leadership of those to whom we had too lazily given the places of mark in that rather childish old world before the smash came.

Some of the chief ingredients in the new temper are a more vigilant scepticism; a new impatience of strident enunciations of vague, venerable, political principles; a rough instinctive application of something like the new philosophy of pragmatism to all questions; and an elated sense of the speed and completeness with which institutions and powers apparently founded on rock can be scoured away. Great masses of men have become more freely critical of the claims of institutions and political creeds and parties which they used to accept without much scrutiny. It is not a temper that need be regarded with terror or reprobation. In itself it is neither good nor bad. It is the raw material of either good or evil, accordingly as it is guided—of barren destruction or of bold repair and improvement. But it is formidable. For men who have seen cities pounded to rubble, men who with little aid or guidance from their own rulers have chased emperors from their thrones, are pretty fully disengaged, at last, from the Englishman's old sense of immutable fixity in institutions which he may find irksome or worthless. 'There's comfort yet. They are assailable.' If the Holy Roman Empire has been knocked into smithereens, what public nuisance need remain?

Chapter VII

'CAN'T BELIEVE A WORD'

(1)

IF you cannot hit or kick during a fight, at any rate you can spit. But, to be happy in this arm of the service, you have to feel sure that the adversary is signally fit to be spat upon. Hence, on each side in every war, the civilian will-to-believe that the other side are a set of ogres, every man of them. What a capital fiend the Boer, the man like Botha or Smuts, was made out to be during the last Boer War! He abused the white flag, he sawed a woman in two, he advanced behind screens of niggers; O, he was a great fellow! In 1870 French civilians laid freely to their souls the flattering unction that the Prussians murdered their prisoners. Strong in what was at bottom the same joyous faith, German civilians told you that French officers usually broke their parole. A few choice spirits will even carry this fond observance into the milder climate of sport. A boy of this kidney, while looking on at a vital house match, will give his mind ease by telling a friend what 'a lot of stinkers' the other house are. A follower of Cambridge cricket, a man of fifty, in whom you might expect the choler of youth to have cooled, has been found musing darkly over a large photograph of an Oxford eleven. They seemed to me, as is the way of these heroes, to lack nothing of outward charm except the light of intellect in the eye. But 'Look at them!' he observed with conviction. 'The hangdog expressions! The narrow, ill-set Mongol eyes! The thin, cruel lips! Prejudice apart, would you like to meet that gang in a quiet place on a dark night?' From these sombre reflections he seemed to derive a sort of pasture.

Little doubt, then, as to what had to come when five of the greatest nations on earth were suddenly rolling over and under each other in the dust. While their armies saw to the biting, the snarling was done with a will by the press of Berlin and Vienna, Petrograd, Paris, and London. That we were all fighting foul,

71

every man, was the burden of the strain. Phone and anti-phone,
the choric hymn of detraction swelled; if this had been an age of
simpler faith there might have been serious fear lest the music
should reach the ear of some Jove sitting at his nectar; what if he
should say in a rage that those nasty little beasts were at it again,
and throw such a comet down on the earth as would settle the
hash of us all? But no such fears troubled Europe. And then
policy, viewing these operations of instinct, was moved to cut
in. Official propaganda began, and one of its stock lines was to
help in stoking these fires in the non-combatant heart.

(II)

Some of the fuel to hand was fine. The German command fed
the best of it all into our bunkers, gratis. It owned that its
'frightfulness' plan was no slip, no 'indiscretion of a subordinate,'
but a policy weighed and picked out—worse than that, an em-
bodied ethical doctrine. A Frenchman, when he is cross with
our English virtue, will say that none of us can steal a goose without saying he does it for the public good. But the fey rulers of
Germany could not even be content to say it was an act of moral
beauty to sink the *Lusitania* or to burn Louvain. They must go
on to boast that these scrubby actions were pieces of sound, hard
thinking, the only tenable conclusions to impregnable syllogisms.
Besides man's natural aversion to cruel acts, they thus incurred
his still more universal distaste for pedants. They delivered themselves into our hand. They were beautiful butts, ready made, like
the learned elderly lady in *Roderick Random*, whose bookish
philosophy made her desire to 'drag the parent by the hoary hair,'
and to 'toss the sprawling infant on her spear.'

But man, rash man, must always be trying to go one better than
the best. With this thing of beauty there for our use, crying out
to be used, some of our propagandists must needs go beyond it
and try to make out that the average German soldier, the docile
blond with yellow hair, long skull, and blue, woolgathersome
eyes, who swarmed in our corps cages during the last two years
of the war, craving for some one, anyone, to give him an order,
was one of the monsters who hang about the gates of Vergil's
Hell. If you had to make out a good hanging case against Ger-

many could you, as Hamlet asks his injudicious mother, on that fair mountain cease to feed and batten on this moor? And yet some of us did. The authentic scarecrow, the school of thought that ruled the old German State, was not used for half of what it was worth. But the word went forth that any redeeming traits in the individual German conscript were better hushed up. When he showed extreme courage in an attack, not much must be made of it. When he behaved well to a wounded Englishman, it must be hidden. A war correspondent who mentioned some chivalrous act that a German had done to an Englishman during an action received a rebuking wire from his employer, 'Don't want to hear about any nice, good Germans.'

Even in the very temple of humourless shabbiness comedy may contrive to keep up a little shrine of her own, and on this forlorn altar the dread of 'crying up anything German' laid, now and then, an undesigned offering. One worthy field censor was suddenly taken aback by a dangerous flaw in a war correspondent's exultant account of a swiftly successful British attack. 'Within ten minutes from zero,' I think the correspondent had written, 'our men were sitting at ease on what had been the enemy's parapet, smoking good German cigars.' 'Hullo!' said the censor, 'this won't do. "Good German cigars." *Good* German cigars! No! "Good" must come out.' And come out it did. Like the *moral* of his troops, like the generalship of his chiefs, the foeman's tobacco had to be bad. It was the time when some of our patriotic pundits found out that Mommsen's Roman history was all wrong, and that Poppo did not half know his Thucydides.

(III)

Of all this kind of swordsmanship the most dashing feat was the circulation of the 'corpse factory' story. German troops, it was written in part of our Press, had got, in certain places near their front, a proper plant for boiling down the fat of their own dead. It was not said whether the product was to be used as a food, or as a lubricant or illuminant only. Chance brought me into one of the reputed seats of this refinement of frugality. It was on ground that our troops had just taken, in 1918. At Bellincourt the St Quentin Canal goes into a long tunnel. Some little way in from its mouth you could find, with a flash-lamp, a small doorway cut in the tunnel's brick wall, on the tow-path side of the canal. The doorway led to the foot of a narrow staircase that wound up through the earth till it came to an end in a room about twenty feet long. It, too, was subterranean, but now its darkness was pierced by one sharp-edged shaft of sunlight let in through a neat round hole cut in the five or six feet of earth above. Loaves, bits of meat, and articles of German equipment lay scattered about, and two big dixies or cauldrons, like those in which we stewed our tea, hung over two heaps of cold charcoal. Eight or ten bodies, lying pell-mell, nearly covered half of the floor. They showed the usual effects of shell-fire. Another body, disembowelled and blown almost to rags, lay across one of the dixies and mixed with the puddle of coffee that it contained. A quite simple case. Shells had gone into cook-houses of ours, long before then, and had messed up the cooks with the stew.

An Australian sergeant, off duty and poking about, like a good Australian, for something to see, had come up the stairs, too. He had heard the great fat-boiling yarn, and how this was the latest seat of the industry. Sadly he surveyed the disappointing scene. Ruefully he noted the hopelessly normal nature of all the proceedings that had produced it. Then he broke the silence in which we had made our several inspections. 'Can't believe a word you read, sir, can you?' he said with some bitterness. Life had failed to yield one of its advertised marvels. The Press had lied again. The propagandist myth about Germans had cracked up once more. 'Can't believe a word you read' had long been becoming a kind of catch-phrase in the army. And now another good man had been duly confirmed in the faith, ordained as a minister of the faith, that whatever your pastors and masters tell you had best be assumed to be just a bellyful of east wind.

(IV)

Partly it came of the nature—which could not be helped by that time—of war correspondence. In the first months of the war our General Staff, being what we had made it, treated British war correspondents as pariah dogs. They might escape arrest so long as they kept out of sight; that was about the sum of their privileges. Long before the end of the war the Chiefs of Staff of our several armies received them regularly on the eve of every battle, explained to them the whole of our plans and hopes, gave them copies of our most secret objective and barrage maps; every perilous secret we had was put into their keeping. A little later still an Army Commander would murmur, with very little indistinctness, if he thought the war correspondents had not been writing enough about his army of late. After the Armistice Sir Douglas Haig made them a speech of thanks and praise on the great bridge over the Rhine at Cologne, and at the Peace all the regular pariah dogs were offered knighthoods.

The Regular Army had set out by taking a war correspondent to be, *ex officio*, a low fellow paid to extract kitchen literature from such private concerns of the military profession as wars. It harboured the curious notion that it would be possible in this century to feed the nation at home on *communiqués* from G.H.Q. alone or eked out with 'Eye-Witness' stuff—official 'word-painting' by some Regular Officer with a tincture of letters. With that power of learning things, only just not too late, which distinguishes our Regular Army from the Bourbons, it presently saw that this plan had broken down. About the same time the Regular Army began to recognize in the abhorred war correspondent a man whom it had known at school, and who had gone to the university about the time when it, the Army, was going into the Army Class. That was enough. Foul as was his profession, still he might be a decent fellow; he might not want to injure his country.

When these reflections were dawning slowly over the Regular Army mind it happened—Sir Douglas Haig having a mind himself—that his Chief of Intelligence was a fully educated man with a good fifty per cent. more of brains, imagination, decision, and initiative than the average of his fellow-Regulars on the Staff. He knew something of the Press at first hand. Being a Scotsman, he regarded writers and well-read people with interest and not with alarm. Under his command the policy of helping the Press rose to its maximum. War correspondents were given the 'status,' almost the rank, of officers. Actual officers were detailed to see to their comfort, to pilot them about the front, to secure their friendly treatment by all ranks and at all headquarters. Never were war correspondents so helped, shielded and petted before. And, almost without an exception, they were good men. Only one or two black sheep of the trade would try to make a reader believe that they had seen things which they had not. The general level of personal and professional honour, of courage, public spirit, and serious enterprise, was high. No average Staff Officer could talk with the average British correspondent without feeling that this was a sound human being and had a better mind than his own—that he knew more, had seen more, and had been less deadened by the coolie work of a professional routine. When once known, the war correspondents were trusted and liked—by the Staff.

(V)

There lay the trouble. They lived in the Staff world, its joys and its sorrows, not in the combatant world. The Staff was both their friend and their censor. How could they show it up when it failed? One of the first rules of field censorship was that from war correspondents 'there must be no criticism of authority or command'; how could they disobey that? They would visit the front now and then, as many Staff Officers did, but it could be only as afternoon callers from one of the many mansions of G.H.Q., that heaven of security and comfort. When autumn twilight came down on the haggard trench world of which they had caught a quiet noon-day glimpse they would be speeding west in Vauxhall cars to lighted châteaux gleaming white among scatheless woods. Their staple emotions before a battle were of necessity akin to those of the Staff, the racehorse-owner or trainer exalted with brilliant hopes, thrilled by the glorious uncertainty of the game, the fascinating nicety of every preparation, and feeling the presence of horrible fatigues and the nearness of multitudinous deaths chiefly as a dim, sombre background that added importance to the rousing scene, and not as things that need seriously cloud the spirit or qualify delight in a plan.

'Our casualties will be enormous,' a General at G.H.Q. said with the utmost serenity on the eve of one of our great attacks in 1917. The average war correspondent—there were golden exceptions—insensibly acquired the same cheerfulness in face of vicarious torment and danger. In his work it came out at times in a certain jauntiness of tone that roused the fighting troops to fury against the writer. Through his despatches there ran a brisk implication that regimental officers and men enjoyed nothing better than 'going over the top'; that a battle was just a rough, jovial picnic; that a fight never went on long enough for the men; that their only fear was lest the war should end on this side of the Rhine. This, the men reflected in helpless anger, was what people at home were offered as faithful accounts of what their friends in the field were thinking and suffering.

Most of the men had, all their lives, been accepting 'what it says 'ere in the paper' as being presumptively true. They had taken the Press at its word without checking. Bets had been settled by reference to a paper. Now, in the biggest event of their lives, hundreds of thousands of men were able to check for themselves the truth of that workaday Bible. They fought in a battle or raid, and two days after they read, with jeers on their lips, the account of 'the show' in the papers. They felt they had found the Press out. The most bloody defeat in the history of Britain, a very world's wonder of valour frustrated by feckless misuse, of regimental glory and Staff shame, might occur on the Ancre on July 1, 1916, and our Press come out bland and copious and graphic, with nothing to show that we had not had quite a good day—a victory really. Men who had lived through the massacre read the stuff open-mouthed. Anything, then, could figure as anything else in the Press—as its own opposite even. Black was only an aspect of white. With a grin at the way he must have been taken in up to now, the fighting soldier gave the Press up. So it comes that each of several million ex-soldiers now reads every solemn appeal of a Government, each beautiful speech of a Premier or earnest assurance of a body of employers with that maxim on guard in his mind—'You can't believe a word you read.'

Chapter VIII

THE DUTY OF LYING

(1)

To fool the other side has always been fair in a game. Every fencer or boxer may feint. A Rugby football player 'gives the dummy' without any shame. In cricket a bowler is justly valued the more for masking his action.

In war your licence to lead the other fellow astray is yet more ample. For war, though it may be good sport to some men, is not a mere sport. In sport you are not 'out to win' except on certain terms of courtesy and handsomeness. Who would take pride in a race won by a fluke? At Henley, a long time ago, there were five or six scullers in for the Diamonds. One of them, L——, was known to be far the best man in the race. In the first heat he was drawn against A——, of Oxford, about the best of the others. L—— had one fault—a blind eye; and it often made him steer a bad course. Before the two had raced for fifty yards L—— blundered out of his course, crashed into A——, and capsized him. The rules of boat-racing are clear: L—— had done for himself. A——, who was now swimming, had only to look up to the umpire's launch and hold up a hand. A nod would have been the reply, and the heat would have been A——'s, and the final heat, in all likelihood, too. A—— looked well away from the umpire and kept his hands down, got back into his boat and said to his contrite opponent, 'Start again here, sir?' A—— was decisively beaten, and never came so near to winning the Diamonds again.

Of course he was right, the race being sport. He had 'loved the game beyond the prize'; he had, like Cyrano, *emporté son panache;* he had seen that in sport the thing to strive for is prowess itself, and not its metallic symbol. But the prize of victory in war is no symbol; it is the thing itself, the real end and aim of all that you do and endure. If A—— had been sculling not for a piece of silversmith's work but for the righting of a wronged nation or for the reassertion of public right throughout

Europe, not only would he have been morally free to take a lucky fluke when he got it: he would not have been morally free to reject it. In war you have to 'play to win'—words of sinister import in sport. Pot-hunting, unhonoured in sport, is a duty in war, where the pot is, perhaps, the chance of a free life for your children.

Hence your immemorial right to fall on your enemy where he is weak, to start before he is ready, to push him out of the course, to jockey him on the rails, to use against him all three of Bacon's recipes for deceiving. A good spy will lie to the last, and in war a prisoner may lie like a saint and hero. With unmistakable glee the Old Testament tells us of Gideon's excellent practical fib with the crockery and trumpets. Even the Wooden Horse of the Greeks has long ceased to raise moral questions. The pious Aeneas, certainly, called it a foul. But what did he do himself, when he got a good opening? Went, as the Irish say, beyond the beyonds and fought in an enemy uniform. Ruses of war and war lies are as ancient as war itself, and as respectable. The most innocent animals use them; they shammed dead in battle long before Falstaff.

The only new thing about deception in war is modern man's more perfect means for its practice. The thing has become, in his hand, a trumpet more efficacious than Gideon's own. When Sinon set out to palm off on the Trojans the false news of a Greek total withdrawal, that first of Intelligence officers made a venture like that of early man, with his flint-headed arrow, accosting a lion. Sinon's pathetic little armament of yarns, to be slung at his proper peril, was frailer than David's five stones from the brook. Modern man is far better off. To match the Lewis gun with which he now fires his solids, he has to his hand the newspaper Press, a weapon which fires as fast as the Lewis itself, and is almost as easy to load whenever he needs, in his wars, to let fly at the enemy's head the thing which is not.

He has this happiness, too: however often he fires, he can, in a sense, never miss. He knows that while he is trying to feed the enemy with whatever it may be bad for him to read the enemy will be trying just as hard to leave no word of it unread. As busily as your enemy's telescopes will be conning your lines in the field, his Intelligence will be scrutinizing whatever is said in

your Press, worrying out what it means and which of the things
that it seems to let out are the traps and which are the real, the
luminous, priceless slips made in unwariness. What the Sphinx
was to her *clientèle*, what the sky is to mountain-climbers and
sailors, your Press is to him: an endless riddle, to be interrogated
and interpreted for dear life. His wits have to be at work on it
always. Like a starved rat in a house where rat-poison is laid, he
can afford neither to nibble a crumb that has got the virus on it,
nor yet to leave uneaten any clean crumb that has fallen accidentally from a table. Do not thrilling possibilities open before
you?

> *What cannot you and I perform upon*
> *The unguarded Duncan? What not put upon*
> *His spongy officers?*

—that is, if Duncan be really unguarded enough to 'ravin down
his proper bane,' like a dutiful rat, and his officers spongy enough
to sop up, according to plan, the medicated stuff that you give
them.

(II)

It is the common habit of nations at war to ascribe to the other
side all the cunning, as if the possession of a Ulysses were some
sort of discredit. Happily for us our chosen Ulysses in France, at
the most critical time, was of the first order. But no soldier can
go far ahead of his time; he has to work in it and with it. And so
the rich new mine of Intelligence work through the Press was
not worked by either side, in the Great War, for all it was worth.
Only a few trial borings were made; experimental shafts were
sunk into the seam, and good, promising stuff was brought to
the top.

Here are a couple of samples. Some readers of popular science,
as it is called, may have been shocked to see in a technical journal,
rather late in the war, a recklessly full description of our 'listening sets'—the apparatus by which an enemy telephone message
is overheard in the field. 'Why,' they must have thought, 'this is
giving away one of our subtlest devices for finding out what the
enemy is about. The journal ought to be prosecuted.' The article

had really come from G.H.Q. It was the last thrust in a long duel.

When the war opened the Germans had good apparatus for telephonic eavesdropping. We had, as usual, nothing to speak of. The most distinctly traceable result was the annihilation of our first attack at Ovillers, near Albert, early in July 1916. At the instant fixed for the attack our front at the spot was smothered under a bombardment which left us with no men to make it. A few days after, when we took Ovillers, we found the piece of paper on which the man with the German 'listening set' had put down, word for word, our orders for the first assault. Then we got to work. We drew our own telephones back, and we perfected our own 'listening sets' till the enemy drew back his, further and further, giving up more and more of ease and rapidity of communication in order to be safe. At last a point was reached at which he had backed right out of hearing. All hope of pushing him back further still, by proving in practice that we could still overhear, was now gone. All that was left to do was to add the effects of a final bluff to the previous effects of the real strength of our hand. And so there slipped into a rather out-of-the-way English journal the indiscretion by which the reach of our electric ears was, to say the least of it, not understated. Few people in England might notice the article. The enemy could be trusted to do so.

When the Flanders battle of July 31, 1917, was about to be fought, we employed the old ruse of the Chinese attack. We modernized the trick of mediæval garrisons which would make a show of getting ready to break out at one gate when a real sally was to be made from another. The enemy was invited to think that a big attack was at hand. But against Lens, and not east of Ypres. Due circumstantial evidence was provided. There were audible signs that a great concentration of British guns were cautiously registering, west of Lens. A little scuffle on that part of the front elicited from our side an amazing bombardment—apparently loosed in a moment of panic. I fancy a British Staff Officer's body—to judge by his brassard and tabs—may have floated down the Scarpe into the German lines. Interpreted with German thoroughness, the maps and papers upon it might easily betray the fact that Lens was the objective. And then a really inexcusable indiscretion appeared—just for a moment, and then was hushed up—in the London Press. To an acute German eye it must have been obvious that this composition was just the inconsequent gassing of some typically stupid English General at home on leave; he was clearly throwing his weight about, as they say, without any real understanding of anything. The stuff was of no serious value, except for one parenthetic, accidental allusion to Lens as the mark. As far as I know, this ebullition of babble was printed in only one small edition of one London paper. Authority was then seen to be nervously trying, as Uncle Toby advised, 'to wipe it up and say no more about it.' Lest it should not be observed to have taken this wise precaution some fussy member of Parliament may have asked in the House of Commons how so outrageous a breach of soldierly reticence had occurred. And was there no control over the Press? It all answered. The Germans kept their guns in force at Lens, and their counter barrage east of Ypres was so much the lighter, and our losses so much the less.

(III)

If we did these things in the green leaf, what might we not do in the dry? Mobilize our whole Press, conscribe it for active service under a single control, a—let us be frank—a Father-General of Lies, the unshaming strategic and tactical lies of 'the great wars' which 'make ambition virtue,' and sometimes make mendacity a virtue too? Coach the whole multitudinous orchestra of the Press to carry out the vast conceptions of some consummate conductor, *splendide mendax*? From each instrument under his baton this artist would draw its utmost contributive aid to immense schemes of concerted delusiveness, the harping of the sirens elaborated into Wagnerian prodigies of volume and complexity.

As you gaze from the top of a tree or a tower behind your own front, in a modern war, all the landscape beyond it looks as if man had perished from the earth, leaving his works behind him. It all looks strangely vacant and dead, the roofs of farms and the spires of churches serving only to deepen your sense of this blank deletion of man, as the Roman arches enhance the vacuous stillness of the Campagna. Your Intelligence Corps has to convert this first impression, this empty page, into a picture, built up line by line, dot by dot, of the universe of activities that are going on out there. Its first and easiest task is to mark out correctly the place where every enemy unit is, each division, each battery, each railhead, aerodrome, field hospital and dump. Next it has to mark each movement of each of these, the shiftings of the various centres of gravity, the changes in the relative density and relative quality of troops and guns at various sectors, the increase, at any sector, of field hospitals, the surest harbingers of heavy attacks. The trains on all lines must be counted, their loads calculated. Next must be known in what sort of spirits the enemy is, in the field and also at home. Do the men believe in their officers? Do the men get confident letters from their civilian friends? Do they send cheerful ones back? Is desertion rare and much abhorred? Or so common that men are no longer shot for it now? So you may go on enumerating until it strikes you that you are simply drifting into an inventory of all the details of the enemy's war-time life, in the field and at home. And then you understand.

For what you want to know, in order to beat him, is no less than this—to see him steadily and see him whole. In the past we have talked of information 'of military value' as distinct from other information. But all information about either side is of military value to the other. News of the outbreak or settlement of a strike in a Welsh coalfield was of military value to Ludendorff. News of the day's weather in Central Europe was of military value to Sir Douglas Haig. News of anything that expressed in any degree the temper of London or Berlin, of Munich or Manchester, helped to eke out that accurate vision of an enemy's body and mind which is the basis of success in combat. A black dot, of the size of a pin-head, may seem, when looked at alone, to give no secret away. But when the same dot is seen, no longer in isolation, but as part of a pen-and-ink drawing, perhaps it may leap into vital prominence, showing now as the pupil of the eye that completes a whole portrait, gives its expression to a face and identifies a sitter. Throughout the Great War our own Press and that of the Germans were each pouring out, for the undesigned benefit of their enemy, substantially correct descriptions of everything in the war life of their respective nations, except a few formal military and naval secrets specially reserved by the censors. Each nation fought, on the whole, with the other standing well out in the light with no inscrutability about its countenance. If we were ever again in such risk of our national life, would we not seriously try to make ourselves an enigma? Or would we leave this, as we have left some other refinements of war, to the other side to introduce first?

(IV)

Suppose us again at war with a Power less strong at sea than ourselves. If we should want its fleet to come out and fight in the open, why not evoke, some fine morning, from every voice in our daily press, a sudden and seemingly irrepressible cry of grief and rage over the unconcealable news—the Censor might be defied by the way—that our Grand Fleet, while ranging the seas, had struck a whole school of drift mines and lost half its numbers? Strategic camouflage, however, would go far beyond such special means to special ends as that. It would, as a regular thing, derange the whole landscape presented to enemy eyes by our Press. There was in the war a French aerodrome across which the French camouflage painters had simply painted a great white high-road: it ran across hangars, huts, turf, everything; and everything was amazingly obliterated by it. Across our real life, as seen under the noon-day rays of publicity in ordinary times, the supreme controller might draw some such enormous lines of falsification.

Most of the fibs that we used in the war were mere nothings, and clumsy at that. When the enemy raided our trenches in the dead winter season, took fifty prisoners, and did as he liked for a while—so much as he liked that a court of inquiry was afterwards held and a colonel deprived of his command—we said in our official *communiqué* that a hostile raiding party had 'entered our trenches' but was 'speedily driven out, leaving a number of dead.' When civilian *moral* at home was going through one of its occasional depressions, we gave out that it was higher than ever. We did not officially summon from the vast deep the myth about Russian soldiers in England. But when it arose out of nothing we did make some use of it. These were, however, little more than bare admissions of the principle that truthfulness in war is not imperative. Falsification was tried, but it was not 'tried out.' Like really long-range guns, the kindred of 'Bertha,' it came into use only enough to suggest what another world-war might be. *Vidimus tantum*. And then the war ended.

Under a perfected propaganda system the whole surface presented by a country's Press to the enemy's Intelligence would be a kind of painted canvas. The artist would not merely be reticent about the positions, say, of our great training camps. He would create, by indirect evidence, great dummy training camps. In the field we had plenty of dummy aerodromes, with hangars complete and a few dummy machines sprawling outside, to draw enemy bomb-fire. At home we would have dummy Salisbury Plains to which a guarded allusion would peep out here and there while the new unity of command over the Press would delete the minutest clue to the realities. Episodes like that of the famous Lansdowne letter would not be left for nature to bungle. If at any time such an episode seemed likely to touch any diplomatic spring with good strategic effect, it would happen at that moment and no other. Otherwise it would not happen, so far as any trace of it in the Press could betray. By-elections, again, their course and result, may tell an enemy much of what your people are thinking. But, for military purposes, there is always some particular thing which you want him to believe them to be thinking. So you would not leave it to the capricious chances of an actual election to settle whether he should be led to believe this or not. You would see to it. Just as you camouflage your real guns and expose dummy guns, so you would obliterate from the Press all trace of your real elections and offer to view, at the times that best suited, dummy elections, *ad hoc* elections, complete in all their parts.

We have imagined a case in which it would be our interest to raise false confidence in the enemy, perhaps to draw a hurried attack on our shores at a time of our own choosing. Then, if the whole of our Press is held in our hand like a fiddle, ready to take and give out any tune, what should prevent us from letting fall, in sudden distress, a hundred doleful, forced admissions that the strain has proved too great, the smash has come, the head of the State is in hiding from his troops, the Premier in flight, naval officers hanging from modern equivalents to the yard-arm,

Ministers and Commanders-in-Chief shaking their fists in one another's faces? Or take the opposite case, that you mean to attack in force, in the field. Here you would add to the preliminary bombardment of your guns such a bombardment of assertion and insinuation, not disprovable before 'zero' hour, as has never yet been essayed; plausible proofs from neutral quarters that the enemy's troops are being betrayed by their politicians behind, that typhus has broken out among the men's homes, that their children are dying like flies, and some of the mothers, insane with famine and grief, are eating the dead in hope of nursing the living. Oh, you could say a great deal.

And you could deliver your messages, too. The enemy's command might try to keep the contents of your Press from reaching his troops. But, thanks to the aeroplane, you can circularize the enemy's troops almost as easily as traders can canvass custom at home. You can flood his front line with leaflets, speeches, promises, rumours, and caricatures. You can megaphone to it. Only in recent years has human ingenuity thought of converting the older and tamer form of political strife into the pandemonic 'stunt' of a 'whirlwind election.' Shall war not have her whirlwind canvasses no less renowned than those of peace? Some rather shamefaced passages of love there have been between us and the Rumour of Shakespeare, the person 'painted full of tongues,' who 'stuffs the ears of men with false reports,' to the advantage of her wooers. Why not espouse the good lady right out? Make an honest woman of her?

(V)

Perhaps you would shrink back. Perhaps at any rate you do so now, when for the moment this great implement is not being offered to you, to take or leave, at an instant crisis of your country's fate. You feel that even in such a case you would stand loftily aloof in your cold purity? You would disclaim as a low, unknightly business the uttering of such base coinage as cooked news, whatever your proud chastity may cost anyone else? Or arrive, perhaps, at the same result by a different route, and make out to yourself that really it pays, in the end, to be decent; that clean chivalry is a good investment at bottom, and that a nation of Galahads and Bayards is sure to come out on top, on the canny reckoning that the body housing a pure heart has got the strength of ten? That is one possible course. And the other is to accept, with all that it implies, the doctrine that there is one morality for peace and another morality for war; that just as in war you may with the clearest conscience stab a man in the back, or kick him in the bowels, in spite of all the sportsmanship you learnt at school, so you may stainlessly carry deception to lengths which in peace would get you blackballed at a club and cut by your friends.

It may be too much to hope that, whichever of these two paths we may choose, we shall tread it with a will. We have failed so much in the way of what Germany used to call 'halfness,' the fault of Macbeth, the wish to hunt with the hounds while we run with the hare, that it would be strange if we did not still try to play Bayard and Ulysses as one man and succeed in combining the shortcomings of an inefficient serpent with those of a sophisticated dove. If we really went the whole serpent the first day of any new war would see a wide, opaque veil of false news drawn over the whole face of our country. Authority playing on all the keys, white and black, of the Press as upon one piano, would give the listening enemy the queerest of Ariel's tunes to follow. All that we did, all that we thought, would be bafflingly falsified. The whole landscape of life in this island, as it reflects itself in the waters of the Press, would come out suddenly altered as far past recognition as that physical landscape amid which it is passed has been changed by a million years of sunshine, rain, and frost. The whole sky would be darkened with flights of strategic and tactical lies so dense that the enemy would fight in a veritable 'fog of war' darker than London's own November brews, and the world would feel that not only the Angel of Death was abroad, but the Angel of Delusion too, and would almost hear the beating of two pairs of wings.

(VI)

Well—and then? Any weapon you use in a war leaves some bill to be settled in peace, and the Propaganda arm has its cost like another. To say so is not to say, without more ado, that it should not be used. Its cost should be duly cast up, like our other

accounts; that is all. We all agree—with a certain demur from
the Quakers—that one morality has to be practised in peace and
another in war; that the same bodily act may be wrong in the
one and right in the other. So, to be perfect, you need to have
two gears to your morals, and drive on the one gear in war and
on the other in peace. While you are on the peace gear you must
not even shoot a bird sitting. At the last stroke of some August
midnight you clap on the war gear and thenceforth you may
shoot a man sitting or sleeping or any way you can get him,
provided you and he be soldiers on opposite sides.

Now, in a well-made car, in the prime of its life, there is nothing to keep you from passing straight and conclusively from
one gear to another. The change once made, the new gear continues in force and does not wobble back fitfully and incalculably
into the old. But in matters of conduct you cannot, somehow,
drive long on one gear without letting the other become notice-
ably rusty, stiff, and disinclined to act. It was found in the Great
War that after a long period of peace and general saturation with
peace morals it took some time to release the average English
youth from his indurated distaste for stabbing men in the bowels.
Conversely it has been found of late, in Ireland and elsewhere,
that, after some years of effort to get our youth off the no-
homicide gear, they cannot all be got quickly back to it either,
some of them still being prone to kill, as the French say, *paisible-
ment*, with a lightness of heart that embarrasses statesmen.

We must, to be on the conservative side, assume that the same
phenomenon would attend a post-war effort to bring back to the
truth gear of peace a Press that we had driven for some years on
the war gear of untruthfulness. Indeed, we are not wholly left to
assumption and speculation. During the war the art of Propaganda was little more than born. The various inspired articles-
with-a-purpose, military or political, hardly went beyond the
vagitus, the earliest cry of the new-born method, as yet

> *An infant crying in the night,*
> *And with no language but a cry.*

Yet for more than three years since the Armistice our rulers have
continued to issue to the Press, at our cost as Blue Books and
White Papers, long passages of argument and suggestion almost

fantastically different from the dry and dignified official publications of the pre-war days. English people used to feel a sovereign contempt for the 'semi-official' journalism of Germany and Russia. But the war has left us with a Press at any rate intermittently inspired. What would be left by a war in which Propaganda had come of age and the State had used the Press, as camouflaging material, for all it was worth?

It used at one time to be a great joke—and a source of gain sometimes—among little boys to take it as a benign moral law that so long as you said a thing 'over the left,' it did not matter whether it was true or not. If, to gain your private ends, or to make a fool of somebody else, you wanted to utter a fib, all that you had to do was to append to it these three incantatory words, under your breath, or indeed without any sound or move of your lips at all, but just to yourself in the sessions of sweet silent thought. Then you were blameless. You had cut yourself free, under the rules, from the vulgar morality. War confers on those who wage it much the same self-dispensing power. They can absolve themselves of a good many sins. Persuade yourself that you are at war with somebody else and you find your moral liberty expanding almost faster than you can use it. An Irishman in a fury with England says to himself 'State of war—that's what it is,' and then finds he can go out and shoot a passing policeman from behind a hedge without the discomfort of feeling base. The policeman's comrades say to themselves 'State of war—that's what it has come to,' and go out and burn some other Irishman's shop without a sense of doing anything wrong, either. They all do it 'over the left.' They have stolen the key of the magical garden wherein you may do things that are elsewhere most wicked and yet enjoy the mental peace of the soldier which passeth all understanding.

To kill and to burn may be sore temptations at times, but not so besetting to most men as the temptation to lie is to public speakers and writers. Another frequent temptation of theirs is to live in a world of stale figures of speech, of flags nailed to the mast, of standing to one's guns, of deaths in last ditches, of quarter neither asked nor given. It is their hobby to figure their own secure, squabblesome lives in images taken from war. And their little excesses, their breaches of manners, and even, some-

times, of actual law, are excused, as a rule, in terms of virile
disdain for anything less drastic and stern than the morals of the
real warfare which they know so little. We have to think in
what state we might leave these weak brethren after a long war
in which we had practised them hard in lying for the public good
and also in telling themselves it was all right because of the
existence of a state of war. State of war! Why, that is what every
excitable politician or journalist declares to exist all the time. To
the wild party man the party which he hates is always 'more
deadly than any foreign enemy.' All of us could mention a few
politicians, at least, to whom the Great War was merely a passing
incident or momentary interruption of the more burningly
authentic wars of Irish Orange and Green, or of English Labour
and Capital.

(VII)

Under the new dispensation we should have to appoint on the
declaration of war, if we had not done it already, a large Staff
Department of Press Camouflage. Everything is done best by
those who have practised it longest. The best inventors and dis-
seminators of what was untrue in our hour of need would be
those who had made its manufacture and sale their trade in our
hours of ease. The most disreputable of successful journalists and
'publicity experts' would naturally man the upper grades of the
war staff. The reputable journalists would labour under them,
trying their best to conform, as you say in drill, to the move-
ments of the front rank. For in this new warfare the journalist
untruthful from previous habit and training would have just that
advantage over the journalist of character which the Regular
soldier had over the New Army officer or man in the old. He
would be, as Mr Kipling sings,

> *A man that's too good to be lost you,*
> *A man that is 'andled and made,*
> *A man that will pay what 'e cost you*
> *In learnin' the others their trade.*

After the war was over he would return to his trade with an
immense accession of credit. He would have been decorated and
publicly praised and thanked. Having a readier pen than the mere

combatant soldiers, he would probably write a book to explain that the country had really been saved by himself, though the fighting men were, no doubt, gallant fellows. He would, in all likelihood, have completed the disengagement of his mind from the idea that public opinion is a thing to be dealt with by argument and persuasion, appeals to reason and conscience. He would feel surer than ever that men's and women's minds are most strongly moved not by the leading articles of a paper but by its news, by what they may be led to accept as 'the facts.' So the practice of colouring news, of ordering reporters to take care that they see only such facts as tell in one way, would leap forward. For it would have the potent support of a new moral complacency. When a man feels that his tampering with truth has saved civilization, why should he deny himself, in his private business, the benefit of such moral reflections as this feeling may suggest?

Scott gives, in *Woodstock*, an engaging picture of the man who has 'attained the pitch of believing himself above ordinances.' The independent trooper, Tomkins, finds his own favourite vices fitting delightfully into an exalted theory of moral freedom. In former days, he avows, he had been only 'the most wild, malignant rakehell in Oxfordshire.' Now he is a saint, and can say to the girl whom he wants to debauch:

Stand up, foolish maiden, and listen; and know, in one word, that sin, for which the spirit of man is punished with the vengeance of heaven, lieth not in the corporal act, but in the thought of the sinner. Believe, lovely Phoebe, that to the pure all acts are pure, and that sin is in our thought, not in our actions, even as the radiance of the day is dark to a blind man but seen and enjoyed by him whose eyes receive it. To him who is but a novice in the things of the spirit much is enjoined, much is prohibited; and he is fed with milk fit for babes—for him are ordinances, prohibitions, and commands. But the saint is above all these ordinances and restraints. To him, as to the chosen child of the house, is given the pass-key to open all locks which withhold him from the enjoyment of his heart's desire. Into such pleasant paths will I guide thee, lovely Phoebe, as shall unite in joy, in innocent freedom, pleasures which, to the unprivileged, are sinful and prohibited.

So when a journalist with no strong original predisposition to swear to his own hurt shall have gained high public distinction by his fertility in falsehoods for consumption by an enemy in the field, the fishes that tipple in the deep may well 'know no such liberty' as this expert in fiction will allow himself when restored to his own more intoxicating element.

The general addition of prestige to the controversial device of giving false impressions and raising false issues would naturally be immense. To argue any case merely on its merits and on the facts would seem to the admirers of the new way a kind of virtuous imbecility. In what great industrial dispute or political campaign, in what struggle between great financial interests would both sides, or either, forego the use of munitions so formidable? Such conflicts might almost wholly cease to be competitions in serious argument at all; they might become merely trials of skill in fantastic false pretences, and of expertness in the morbid psychology of credulity.

So men argued, surmised and predicted, talking and talking away in the endless hours that war gives for talking things out. When first they began to ask each other why so many lies were about, the common hypothesis, based on prior experience, was that they must be meant to save some 'dud,' up above, from losing his job. Then they came to admit there was something more in it than that. Lies had a good enough use for fooling the Germans. A beastly expedient, no doubt; acquiescence in lying does not come quite so easily to a workman of good character as it does to men of a class in which more numerous formal fibs are kept in use as social conveniences. Still, the men were not cranks enough to object. 'They love not poison that do poison need.' The men had hated, and still continued to hate, the use of poison gas, too. It was a scrub's trick, like vitriol-throwing. But who could have done without it, when once the Germans began? And now who could object to the use of this printed gas either? Could they, in this new warfare of propaganda, expect their country to go into action armed in a white robe of candour, and nothing besides, like a maskless man going forth to war against a host assisted by phosgene and all her foul sisters?

It was a clear enough case: decency had to go under. But it was hard luck not to be able to know where you were. Where

THE DUTY OF LYING 93

were they? If all the news they could check was mixed with lies, what about all the rest, which they were unable to check? Was it likely to be any truer? Why, we might be losing the war all the time, everywhere! Who could believe now what was said about our catching the submarines? Or about India's being all right? And how far would you have to go to get outside the lie belt? Could our case for going to war with the Germans be partly lies too? Beastly idea!

How would it be, again, when we came to play these major tricks which the men were already discussing as likely to come into use? Suppose it became part of our game to publish, for some good strategical reason, news of a naval or military disaster to ourselves, the same not having happened? To take in the enemy this lie would have to take in our own people too; the ruse would be given away if the Government tried to tip so much as a wink to the British reader of the British Press. So men's friends at home would have the agonies of false alarms added to their normal war-time miseries, and wives might be widowed twice and mothers of one son made childless more than once before the truth finally overshadowed their lives.

And then, your war won, there would be that new lie-infested and infected world of peace. In one of his great passages Thucydides tells us what happened to Greece after some years of war and of the necessary war morality. He says that, as far as veracity, public and private, goes, the peace gear was found to have got wholly out of working order and could not be brought back into use. 'The meaning of words had no longer the same relation to things, but was changed by men as they thought proper.' The pre-war hobby of being straight and not telling people lies went clean out of fashion. Anyone who could bring off a good stroke of deceit, to the injury of some one whom he disliked, 'congratulated himself on having taken the safer course, over-reached his enemy, and gained the prize of superior talent.' A man who did not care to use so sound a means to his ends was thought to be a goody-goody ass. War worked in that way on the soul of Greece, in days when war was still confined, in the main, to the relatively cleanly practice of hitting your enemy over the head, wherever you could find him. The philosophers in our dug-outs preserved moderation when they expected as ugly a sequel for war in our age, when the chivalrous school seems to have pretty well worked itself out and the most promising lines of advance are poison gas and canards. But the survivors among them are not detached philosophers only. They act in the new world that they foresaw, and the man whose word you could trust like your own eyes and ears, eight years ago, has come back with the thought in his mind that so many comrades of his have expressed: 'They tell me we've pulled through at last all right because our proper-gander dished out better lies than what the Germans did. So I say to myself "If tellin' lies is all that bloody good in war, what bloody good is tellin' truth in peace?" '

Chapter IX

AUTUMN COMES

(I)

In the autumn of 1917 the war entered into an autumn, or late middle-age, of its own. 'Your young men,' we are told, 'shall see visions, and your old men shall dream dreams.' The same with whole armies. But middle-aged armies or men may not have the mists of either morning or evening to charm them. So they may feel like Corot, when he had painted away, in a trance of delight, till the last vapour of dawn was dried up by the sun; then he said, 'You can see everything now. Nothing is left,' and knocked off work for the day. There was no knocking off for the army. But that feeling had come. A high time was over, a great light was out; our eyes had lost the use of something, either an odd penetration that they had for a while, or else an odd web that had been woven across them, shutting only ugliness out.

The feeling was apt to come on pretty strong if you lived at the time on the top of the little hill of Cassel, west of Ypres. The Second Army's Headquarters were there. You might, as some Staff duty blew you about the war zone, be watching at day-break one of that autumn's many dour bouts of attrition under the Passchendale Ridge, in the mud, and come back, the same afternoon, to sit in an ancient garden hung on the slope of the hill, where a great many pears were yellowing on the wall and sunflowers gazing fixedly into the sun that was now failing them. All the corn of French Flanders lay cut on the brown plain under your eyes, from Dunkirk, with its shimmering dunes and the glare on the sea, to the forested hills north of Arras. Everywhere lustre, reverie, stillness; the sinking hum of old bees, successful in life and now rather tired; the many windmills fallen motionless, the aureate light musing over the aureate harvest; out in the east the broken white stalks of Poperinghe's towers pensive in haze; and, behind and about you, the tiny hill city, itself in its distant youth the namegiver and prize of three mighty battles that do

95

not matter much now. All these images or seats of outlived ardour, mellowed now with the acquiescence of time in the slowing down of some passionate stir in the sap of a plant or the spirit of insects or men, joined to work on you quietly. There, where the earth and the year were taking so calmly the end of all the grand racket that they had made in their prime, why not come off the high horse that we, too, in that ingenuous season, had ridden so hard? It was not now as it had been of yore. And why pretend that it was?

(II)

One leaf that had gone pretty yellow by now was the hope of perfect victory—swift, unsoured, unruinous, knightly: St George's over the dragon, David's over Goliath. Some people at home seem to be still clinging hard to that first pretty vision of us as a gifted, lithe, wise little Jack fighting down an unwieldy, dastardly giant. But troops in the field become realists. Ours had seen their side visibly swelling for more than two years, till Jack had become a heavier weight than the giant and yet could not finish him off. We knew that our allies and we outnumbered the Germans and theirs. We knew we were just as well armed. We had seen Germans advancing under our fire and made no mistake about what they were worth. Our first vision of victory had gone the way of its frail sister dream of a perfect Allied comradeship. French soldiers sneered at British now, and British at French. Both had the same derisive note in the voice when they named the 'Brav' Belges.' Canadians and Australians had almost ceased to take the pains to break it to us gently that they were the 'storm troops,' the men who had to be sent for to do the tough jobs; that, out of all us sorry home troops, only the Guards Division, two kilted divisions and three English ones could be said to know how to fight. 'The English let us down again'; 'The Tommies gave us a bad flank, as usual'—these were the stirring things you would hear if you called upon an Australian division a few hours after a battle in which the lion had fought by the side of his whelps. Chilly, autumnal things; while you listened, the war was apparelled no longer in the celestial light of its spring.

An old Regular colonel, a man who had done all his work upon the Staff, said, at the time, that 'the war was settling down to peace conditions.' He meant no bitter epigram. He was indeed unfeignedly glad. The war was ceasing to be, like a fire or shipwreck, a leveller of ranks which, he felt, ought not to be levelled. Those whom God had put asunder it was less recklessly joining together. The first wild generosities were cooling off. Not many peers and heirs-apparent to great wealth were becoming hospital orderlies now. Since the first earthquake and tidal wave the disturbed social waters had pretty well found their old seemly levels again; under conscription the sons of the poor were now making privates; the sons of the well-to-do were making officers; sanity was returning. The Regular had faced and disarmed the invading hordes of 1914. No small feat of audacity, either. Think what the shock must have been—what it would be for any profession, just at the golden prime of rich opportunity and searching test, to be overrun of a sudden by hosts of keen amateurs, many of them quick-witted, possibly critical, some of them the best brains of the country, most of them vulgarly void of the old professional habits of mind, almost indecently ready to use new and outlandish means to the new ends of to-day.

But now the stir and the peril were over. The Old Army had won. It had scarcely surrendered a single strong point or good billet; Territorials and New Army toiled at the coolie jobs of its household. It had not even been forced, like kings in times of revolution, to make apparent concessions, to water down the pure milk of the word. It had become only the more intensely itself; never in any war had commands been retained so triumphantly in the hands of the cavalry and the Guards, the leaders and symbols of the Old Army resistance to every inroad of mere professional ardour and knowledge and strong, eager brains. When Sir Francis Lloyd relinquished the London Distict Command a highly composite mess in France discussed possible successors. 'Of course,' said a Guards colonel gravely—and he was a guest in the mess—'the first point is—he *must* be a Guardsman.' Peace conditions returning, you see; the peace frame of mind; the higher commands restored to their ancient status as property, 'livings,' perquisites, the bread of the children, not to be given to dogs. At home, too, peace conditions were taking heart to return. The scattered coveys of profiteers and job-hunters, al-

D

most alarmed by the first shots of the war, had long since met in security; 'depredations as usual' was the word; and the mutual scalping and knifing of politicians had ceased to be shamefaced; who could fairly expect an old Regular Army to practise a more austere virtue than merchant princes and statesmen?

(III)

Even in trenches and near them, where most of the health was, time had begun to embrown the verdant soul of the army. 'Kitchener's Army' was changing. Like every volunteer army, his had sifted itself, at its birth, with the only sieve that will riddle out, even roughly, the best men to be near in a fight. Till the first of the pressed men arrived at our front, a sergeant there, when he posted a sentry and left him alone in the dark, could feel about as complete a moral certitude as there is on the earth that the post would not be let down. For, whatever might happen, nothing inside the man could start whispering to him 'You never asked to be here; if you do fail, it isn't your doing.'

Nine out of ten of the conscripts were equally sound. For they would have been volunteers if they could. The tenth was the problem; the more so because there was nothing to tell you which was the tenth and which were the nine. For all that you knew, any man who came out on a draft, from then on, might be the exception, the literal-minded Christian who thought it wicked to kill in a war; or an anti-nationalist zealot who thought us all equally fools, the Germans and us, to be out there pasturing lice, instead of busy at home taking the hide off the *bourgeois*; or one of those drift wisps of loveless critical mind, attached to no place or people more than another, and just as likely as not to think that the war was our fault and that we ought to be beaten. *Riant avenir!* as a French sergeant said when, in an hour of ease, we were talking over the nature of man, and he told me, in illustration of its diversity, how a section of his had just been enriched with a draft of neurasthenic burglars.

These vulgar considerations of military expediency never seemed to cross the outer rim of the consciousness of many worthies who were engaged at home in shooing the reluctant into the army. If a recalcitrant seemed to be lazy, spiritless, nerveless,

if there was every sign of his making a specially worthless and
troublesome consumer of rations in a trench, then a burning zeal
to inflict this nuisance and danger on some unoffending platoon
in France seemed to invade the ordinary military tribunal. Report
said that the satisfaction of this impulse was called, by the
possessed persons, 'giving Haig the men,' and sometimes, with a
more pungent irony, 'supporting our fellows in the trenches.'
Non tali auxilio nec defensoribus istis. Australia's fellows in the
trenches were suffered to vote themselves out of the risk of
getting any support of the kind. Australia is a democracy. Ours
were not asked whether they wanted to see their trenches employed as a penal settlement to which middle-aged moralists in
England might deport, among other persons, those whom they
felt to be morally the least beautiful of their juniors. So nothing
impeded the pious practice of 'larning toads to be toads.' For the
shirker, the 'kicker,' the 'lawyer,' for all the types of undesirables
that contribute most liberally to the wrinkled appearance of
sergeants, those pious men had the nose of collectors. Wherever
there was a spare fifty yards of British front to be held, they, if
anyone, could find a man likely to go to sleep there on guard, or,
in some cyclonic disturbance of spirit, to throw down his rifle
and light out for the coast, across country.

Such episodes were reasonably few. The inveterate mercy that
guards drunken sailors preserved from the worst disaster the
cranks who had made a virtue of giving their country every bad
soldier they could. And the abounding mercy of most courts-
martial rendered few of the episodes fatal to individual conscripts.
Nor, indeed, was the growth in their frequency after conscription wholly due to the more fantastic tricks played before high
Heaven by some of the Falstaffs who dealt with the Mouldies,
Shadows and Bull-calves. Conscription, in any case, must be
dilution. You may get your water more quickly by throwing the
filter away, but don't hope to keep the quality what it was. And
the finer a New Army unit had been, to begin with, the swifter
the autumnal change. Every first-rate battalion fighting in France
or Belgium lost its whole original numbers over and over again.
First, because in action it spared itself less than the poor ones;
secondly, because the best divisions rightly got the hard jobs.
Going out in the late autumn of 1915, a good battalion with

normal luck might have nearly half its original volunteer strength left after the Battle of the Somme. Drafts of conscripts would fill up the gap, each draft with a listless or enigmatic one-tenth that volunteering had formerly kept at a distance. The Battle of Arras next spring might leave only twenty per cent of the first volunteers, and the autumn battles in Flanders would pretty well finish their business. Seasons returned, but not to that battalion returned the spirit of delight in which it had first learnt to soldier together and set foot together in France and first marched through darkness and ruined villages towards the flaring fair-ground of the front. While a New Army battalion was still very young, and fully convinced that no crowd of men so good to be with had ever been brought together before, it used to be always saying how it would keep things up after the war. No such genial reunions had ever been held as these were to be. But now the few odd men that are left only write to each other at long intervals, feeling almost as if they were raising their voices in an empty church. One of them asks another has he any idea what the battalion was like after Oppy, or Bourlon Wood, or wherever their own knock-out came. Like any other battalion, no doubt—a mere G.C.M. of all conscript battalions; conscription filed down all special features and characters.

Quick waste and renewal are said to be good for the body; the faster you burn up old tissues, by good sweaty work, the better your health; fresh and superior tissue is added unto you all the more merrily. Capital, too, the economists say, must be swiftly used up and reborn, over and over again, to do the most good that it can. And then there is the case of the phœnix—in fact, of all the birds and all the beasts too, for all evolution would seem to be just the dying of something worse, as fast as it can, in order that something better may live in its place. No need for delay in turning your anthropoid apes into Shakespeares and Newtons.

But what if you found, after all your hard work, that not all the deceased cells of your flesh were replaced by new cells of the sort you would like? If some of your good golden pounds should have perished only that inconvertible paper might live? If out of your phœnix's ashes only a commonplace rooster should spring? If evolution were guyed and bedevilled into retrovolution, a process by which the fittest must more and more dwindle

away and the less fit survive them, and species be not multiplied
but made fewer? Something, perhaps, of the sort may go on in
the body in its old age, or in roses in autumn. It must go on in a
volunteer army when it is becoming an army of conscripts during
a war that is highly lethal.

(IV)

The fall of the leaf had brought, too, a sad shortage of heroes—
of highly-placed ones, for, of course, every company had its own,
authenticated beyond any proof that crosses or medals could
give. A few very old Regular privates would say, 'Ah! if we had
Buller here!' Sir Redvers Buller has always remained, in lofty
disregard of conclusive disproof, the Cæsar or Hannibal of the
old Regular private, who sets little store by such heroes of White-
hall and Fleet Street as Roberts and Kitchener. But the chiefs of to-
day left men cold, at the best. The name of at least one was a
by-word. Haig was a name and no more, though a name immune
in a mysterious degree from the general scoffing surmise about
the demerits of higher commands. Few subalterns or men had
seen him. No one knew what he was doing or leaving undone.
But some power, not ourselves, making for charity, seemed to
recommend him to mercy in everyone's judgement; as if, from
wherever he was, nameless waves of some sort rippled out
through an uncharted ether, conveying some virtue exhaled by
that winning incarnation of honour, courage, and kindness who,
seen and heard in the flesh, made you wish to find in him all other
excellent qualities too. The front line gave him all the benefit of
every doubt. God only knew, it said, whether he or somebody
else would have to answer for Bullecourt and Serre. It might not
be he who had left the door lying open, unentered, for two nights
and days, when the lions had won the battle of Arras that spring,
and the asses had let the victory slip till the Germans crept back
in the dark to the fields east of Vimy from which they had fled
in despair. But slowness to judge can hardly be called hero-
worship; at most, a somewhat sere October phase of that vernal
religion.

One of the heavenly things on which the New Army had almost counted, in its green faith, was that our higher commands

would have genius. Of course, we had no right to do it. No X
has any right to ask of Y that Y shall be Alexander the Great or
Bach or Rembrandt or Garrick, or any kind of demonic first-
rater. As reasonably send precepts to the Leviathan to come
ashore. Yet we had indulged that insane expectation, just as we
had taken it for granted that this time the nation would be as
one man, and nobody 'out to do a bit for himself on the quiet.'
And now behold the falling leaf and no Leviathan coming ashore
in response to our May-Day desires.

Certainly other things, highly respectable, came. The Second
Army Staff's direction of that autumn's almost continuous battles
was of a competence passing all British precedents. Leap-frogging
waves of assault, box barrages, creeping barrages, actions, interac-
tions, and counter-actions were timed and concerted as no Staff
of ours had done it before. The intricate dance which has to go
on behind a crowded battle front, so that columns moving east
and west and columns moving north and south shall not coincide
at cross roads, was danced with the circumstantial precision of
the best ballets. An officer cast away somewhere in charge of a
wayside smithy for patching up chipped guns felt that there was
a power perched on the top of the hill at Cassel which smelt out
a bit of good work, or of bad, wherever anyone did it. Sense,
keenness, sympathy, resolution, exactness—all the good things
abode in that eyrie which have to be in attendance before genius
can bring off its marvels; every chamber swept and garnished,
and yet—.

Foch tells us what he thinks Napoleon might have said to the
Allied commands if he could have risen in our black times from
the dead. 'What cards you people have!' he would have said,
'And how little you do with them! Look!' And then, Foch
thinks, within a month or two he 'would have rearranged everything, gone about it all in some new way, thrown out the enemy's
plans and quite crushed him.' That 'some new way' was not fated
to come. The spark refused to fall, the divine accident would not
happen. How could it? you ask with some reason. Had not trench
warfare reached an impasse? Yes; there is always an impasse before genius shows a way through. Music on keyboards had
reached an impasse before a person of genius thought of using his
thumb as well as his fingers. Well, that was an obvious dodge, you

may say, but in Flanders what way through could there have
been? The dodge found by genius is always an obvious dodge,
afterwards. Till it is found it can as little be stated by us common
people as can the words of the poems that Keats might have
written if he had lived longer. You would have to become a Keats
to do that, and a Napoleon to say how Napoleon would have
got through to Bruges in the autumn that seemed so autumnal
to us. All that the army knew, as it decreased in the mud, was
that no such uncovenanted mercy came to transmute its casualties into the swiftly and richly fruitful ones of a Napoleon, the
incidental expenses of some miraculous draught of victory.

Nothing to grouse at in that. The winds of inspiration have to
blow the best way they can. Prospero himself could not raise
them; how could the likes of us hope to? And yet there had
been that illogical hope, almost reliance—part of the high unreason of faith that could move mountains in 1914 and seems to
be scarcely able to shift an ant-hill to-day.

Chapter X

AUTUMN TINTS IN CHIVALRY

(1)

IN either of two opposite tempers you may carry on war. In one of the two you will want to rate your enemy, all round, as high as you can. You may pursue him down a trench, or he you; but in neither case do you care to have him described by somebody far, far away as a fat little short-sighted scrub. Better let him pass for a paladin. This may at bottom be vanity, sentimentality, all sorts of contemptible things. Let him who knows the heart of man be dogmatic about it. Anyhow, this temper comes, as they would say in Ireland, of decent people. It spoke in Porsena of Clusium's whimsical prayer that Horatius might swim the Tiber safely; it animates Velasquez' knightly *Surrender of Breda;* it prompted Lord Roberts's first words to Cronje when Paardeberg fell—'Sir, you have made a very gallant defence'; it is avowed in a popular descant of Newbolt's—

> *To honour, while you strike him down,*
> *The foe who comes with eager eyes.*

The other temper has its niche in letters, too. There was the man that 'wore his dagger in his mouth.' And there was Little Flanigan, the bailiff's man in Goldsmith's play. During one of our old wars with France he was always 'damning the French, the parle-vous, and all that belonged to them.' 'What,' he would ask the company, 'makes the bread rising? The parle-vous that devour us. What makes the mutton fivepence a pound? The parle-vous that eat it up. What makes the beer threepence-halfpenny a pot?'

Well, your first aim in war is to hit your enemy hard, and the question may well be quite open—in which of these tempers can he be hit hardest? If, as we hear, a man's strength be 'as the strength of ten because his heart is pure,' possibly it may add a few foot-pounds to his momentum in an attack if he has kept a

104

clean tongue in his head. And yet the production of heavy woollens in the West Riding, for War Office use, may, for all that we know, have been accelerated by yarns about crucified Canadians and naked bodies of women found in German trenches. There is always so much, so bewilderingly much, to be said on both sides. All I can tell is that during the war the Newbolt spirit seemed on the whole, to have its chief seat in and near our front line, and thence to die down westward all the way to London. There Little Flanigan was enthroned, and, like Montrose, would bear no rival near his throne, so that a man on leave from our trench system stood in some danger of being regarded as little better than one of the wicked. Anyhow, he was a kind of provincial. Not his will, but that of Flanigan, had to be done. For Flanigan was at the centre of things; he had leisure, or else volubility was his trade; and he had got hold of the megaphones.

(II)

In the first months of the war there was any amount of good sportsmanship going; most, of course, among men who had seen already the whites of enemy eyes. I remember the potent emetic effect of Flaniganism upon a little blond Regular subaltern maimed at the first battle of Ypres. 'Pretty measly sample of the sin against the Holy Ghost!' the one-legged child grunted savagely, showing a London paper's comic sketch of a corpulent German running away. The first words I ever heard uttered in palliation of German misdoings in Belgium came from a Regular N.C.O., a Dragoon Guards sergeant, holding forth to a sergeants' mess behind our line. 'We'd have done every damn thing they did,' he averred, 'if it had been we.' I thought him rather extravagant, then. Later on, when the long row of hut hospitals, jammed between the Calais-Paris Railway at Etaples and the great reinforcement camp on the sand-hills above it, was badly bombed from the air, even the wrath of the R.A.M.C. against those who had wedged in its wounded and nurses between two staple targets scarcely exceeded that of our Royal Air Force against war correspondents who said the enemy must have done it on purpose.

Airmen, no doubt, or some of them, went to much greater lengths in the chivalrous line than the rest of us. Many things helped them to do it. Combatant flying was still new enough to be almost wholly an officer's job; the knight took the knocks, and the squire stayed behind and looked after his gear. Air-fighting came to be pretty well the old duel, or else the mediæval mêlée between little picked teams. The clean element, too, may have counted—it always looked a clean job from below, where your airy notions got mixed with trench mud, while the airman seemed like Sylvia in the song, who so excelled 'each mortal thing upon the dull earth dwelling.' Whatever the cause, he excelled in his bearing towards enemies, dead or alive. The funeral that he gave to Richthofen in France was one of the few handsome gestures exchanged in the war. And whenever Little Flanigan at home began squealing aloud that we ought to take some of our airmen off fighting and make them bomb German women and children instead, our airmen's scorn for these ethics of the dirt helped to keep up the flickering hope that the post-war world might not be ignoble.

Even on the dull earth it takes time and pains to get a clean-run boy or young man into a mean frame of mind. A fine N.C.O. of the Grenadier Guards was killed near Laventie—no one knows how—while going over to shake hands with the Germans on Christmas morning. 'What! not shake on Christmas Day?' He would have thought it poor, sulky fighting. Near Armentières at the Christmas of 1914 an incident happened which seemed quite the natural thing to most soldiers then. On Christmas Eve the Germans lit up their front line with Chinese lanterns. Two British officers thereupon walked some way across No Man's Land, hailed the enemy's sentries, and asked for an officer. The German sentries said, 'Go back, or we shall have to shoot.' The Englishmen said 'Not likely!' advanced to the German wire, and asked again for an officer. The sentries held their fire and sent for an officer. With him the Englishmen made a one-day truce, and on Christmas Day the two sides exchanged cigarettes and played football together. The English intended the truce to end with the day, as agreed, but decided not to shoot next day till the enemy did. Next morning the Germans were still to be seen washing and breakfasting outside their wire; so our men,

too, got out of the trench and sat about in the open. One of
them, cleaning his rifle, loosed a shot by accident, and an English
subaltern went to tell the Germans it had not been fired to kill.
The ones he spoke to understood, but as he was walking back a
German somewhere wide on a flank fired and hit him in the
knee, and he has walked lame ever since. Our men took it that
some German sentry had misunderstood our fluke shot. They did
not impute dishonour. The air in such places was strangely clean
in those distant days. During one of the very few months of
open warfare a cavalry private of ours brought in a captive, a
gorgeous specimen of the terrific Prussian Uhlan of tradition.
'But why didn't you put your sword through him?' an officer
asked, who belonged to the school of Froissart less obviously
than the private. 'Well, sir,' the captor replied, 'the gentleman
wasn't looking.'

(III)

At no seat of war will you find it quite easy to live up to
Flanigan's standards of hatred towards an enemy. Reaching a
front, you find that all you want is just to win the war. Soon you
are so taken up with the pursuit of this aim that you are always
forgetting to burn with the gem-like flame of pure fury that fires
the lion-hearted publicist at home.

A soldier might have had the Athanasian ecstasy all right till
he reached the firing line. Every individual German had sunk the
Lusitania; there was none righteous, none. And yet at a front
the holy passion began to ooze out at the ends of his fingers. The
bottom trouble is that you cannot fight a man in the physical
way without somehow touching him. The relation of actual
combatants is a personal one—no doubt, a rude, primitive one,
but still quite advanced as compared with that between a learned
man at Berlin who keeps on saying *Delenda est Britannia!* at the
top of his voice and a learned man in London who keeps on
saying that every German must have a black heart because Cæsar
did not conquer Germany as he did Gaul and Britain. Just let the
round head of a German appear for a passing second, at long intervals, above a hummock of clay in the middle distance. Before you
had made half a dozen sincere efforts to shoot him the fatal germ

of human relationship had begun to find a nidus again: he had acquired in your mind the rudiments of a personal individuality. You would go on trying to shoot him with zest—indeed, with a diminished likelihood of missing, for mere hatred is a flustering emotion. And yet the hatred business had started crumbling. There had begun the insidious change that was to send you home, on your first leave, talking unguardedly of 'old Fritz' or of 'the good old Boche' to the pain of your friends, as if he were a stout dog fox or a real stag of a hare.

The deadliest solvent of your exalted hatreds is laughter. And you can never wholly suppress laughter between two crowds of millions of men standing within earshot of each other along a line of hundreds of miles. There was, in the Loos salient in 1916, a German who, after his meals, would halloo across to an English unit taunts about certain accidents of its birth. None of his British hearers could help laughing at his mistakes, his knowledge, and his English. Nor could the least humorous priest of ill-will have kept his countenance at a relief when the enemy shouted: 'We know you are relieving,' 'No good hiding it,' 'Good-bye, Ox and Bucks,' 'Who's coming in?' and some humorist in the obscure English battalion relieving shouted back, with a terrific assumption of accent, 'Furrst Black Watch!' or 'Th' Oirish Gyards!' and a hush fell at the sound of these great names. Comedy, expelled with a fork by the dignified figure of Quenchless Hate, had begun to steal back of herself.

At home that tragedy queen might do very well; she did not have these tenpenny nails scattered about on her road to puncture the nobly inflated tyres of her chariot. The heroes who spoke up for shooing all the old German governesses into the barbed wire compounds were not exposed to the moral danger of actually hustling, *propria persona*, these formidable ancients. But while Hamilcar at home was swearing Hannibal and all the other little Hamilcars to undying hatred of the foe, an enemy dog might be trotting across to the British front line to sample its rats, and its owner be losing in some British company's eyes his proper quality as an incarnation of all the Satanism of Potsdam and becoming simply 'him that lost the dog.'

If you took his trench it might be no better; perhaps Incarnate Evil had left its bit of food half-cooked, and the muddy straw, where it lay last, was pressed into a hollow by Incarnate Evil's back as by a cat's. Incarnate Evil should not do these things that other people in trenches do. It ought to be more strange and beastly and keep on making *beaux gestes* with its talons and tail, like the proper dragon slain by St George. Perhaps Incarnate Evil was extinct and you went over its pockets. They never contained the right things—no poison to put in our wells, no practical hints for crucifying Canadians; only the usual stuffing of all soldiers' pockets—photographs and tobacco and bits of string and the wife's letters, all about how tramps were always stealing potatoes out of the garden, and how the baby was worse, and was his leave never coming? No good to look at such things.

(IV)

With this guilty weakness gaining upon them our troops drove the Germans from Albert to Mons. There were scandalous scenes on the way. Imagine two hundred German prisoners grinning inside a wire cage while a little Cockney corporal chaffs them in half the dialects of Germany! His father, he says, was a slop tailor in Whitechapel; most of his journeymen came from somewhere or other in Germany—'Ah! and my dad sweated 'em proper,' he says proudly; so the boy learnt all their kinds of talk. He convulses Bavarians now with his flow of Silesian. He fraternizes grossly and jubilantly. Other British soldiers laugh when one of the Germans sings, in return for favours received, the British ballad 'Knocked 'em in the Ol' Kent Road.' By the time our men had marched to the Rhine there was little hatred left in them. How can you hate the small boy who stands at the farm door visibly torn between dread of the invader and deep delight in all soldiers, as soldiers? How shall a man not offer a drink to the first disbanded German soldier who sits next to him in a public house at Cologne, and try to find out if he was ever in the line at the Brickstacks or near the Big Crater? Why, that might have been his dog!

The billeted soldier's immemorial claim on 'a place by the fire' carried on the fell work. It is hopelessly bad for your grand Byronic hates if you sit through whole winter evenings in the abhorred foe's kitchen and the abhorred foe grants you the

uncovenanted mercy of hot coffee and discusses without rancour
the relative daily yields of the British and the German milch cow.
And then comes into play the British soldier's incorrigible pro-
pensity, wherever he be, to form virtuous attachments. 'Love, un-
foiled in the war,' as Sophocles says. The broad road has a
terribly easy gradient. When all the great and wise at Paris were
making peace, as somebody said, with a vengeance, our command
on the Rhine had to send a wire to say that unless something was
done to feed the Germans starving in the slums it could not
answer for discipline in its army; the men were giving their
rations away, and no orders would stop them. Rank 'Pro-
Germanism,' you see—the heresy of Edith Cavell; 'Patriotism is
not enough; I must have no hatred or bitterness in my heart.'
While these men fought on, year after year, they had mostly
been growing more void of mere spite all the time, feeling always
more and more sure that the average German was just a decent
poor devil like everyone else. One trembles to think what the
really first-class haters at home would have said of our army if
they had known at the time.

(V)

Even at places less distant than home the survival of old English
standards of fighting had given some scandal. In that autumn of
the war when our generalship seemed to have explored all its
own talents and found only the means to stage in an orderly way
the greatest possible number of combats of pure attrition, the
crying up of unknightliness became a kind of fashion among a
good many Staff Officers of the higher grades. 'I fancy our
fellows were not taking many prisoners this morning,' a Corps
Commander would say with a complacent grin, on the evening
after a battle. Jocose stories of comic things said by privates when
getting rid of undesired captives became current in messes far
in the rear. The other day I saw in a history of one of the most
gallant of all British divisions an illustration given by the officer
who wrote it of what he believed to be the true martial spirit. It
was the case of a wounded Highlander who had received with
a bomb a German Red Cross orderly who was coming to help
him. A General of some consequence during part of the war

gave a lecture, towards its end, to a body of officers and others
on what he called 'the fighting spirit.' He told with enthusiasm
an anecdote of a captured trench in which some of our men had
been killing off German appellants for quarter. Another German
appearing and putting his hands up, one of our men—so the story
went—called out, ''Ere! Where's 'Arry? 'E ain't 'ad one yet.'
Probably some one had pulled the good general's leg, and the
thing never happened. But he believed it, and deeply approved
the 'blooding' of 'Arry. That, he explained, was the 'fighting
spirit.' Men more versed than he in the actual hand-to-hand business of fighting this war knew that he was mistaken, and that the
spirit of trial by combat and that of pork-butchery are distinct.
But that is of course. The notable thing was that such things
should be said by anyone wearing our uniform. Twenty years
before, if it had been rumoured, you would, without waiting,
have called the rumour a lie invented by some detractor of
England or of her army. Now it passed quite unhissed. It was the
latter-day wisdom. Scrofulous minds at home had long been itch-
ing, publicly and in print, to bomb German women and children
from aeroplanes, and to 'take it out of' German prisoners of war.
Now the disease had even affected some parts of the non-combatant Staff of our army.

(VI)

You know the most often quoted of all passages of Burke.
Indeed, it is only through quotation of it that most of us know
Burke at all—

> But the age of chivalry is gone . . . the unbought grace of
> life, the cheap defence of nations, the nurse of manly sentiment
> and heroic enterprise is gone! It is gone, that sensibility of
> principle, that chastity of honour, which felt a stain like a
> wound, which inspired courage whilst it mitigated ferocity,
> which ennobled whatever it touched, and under which vice
> itself lost half its evil by losing all its grossness.

Burke would never say a thing by halves. And as truth goes by
halves, and declines to be sweeping like rhetoric, Burke made sure
of being wrong to the tune of some fifty per cent. The French

Revolution did not, as his beautiful language implies, confine mankind for the rest of its days to the procreation of curs. And yet his words do give you, in their own lush, Corinthian way, a notion of something that probably did happen, a certain limited shifting of the centre of gravity of West European morals or manners.

One would be talking like Burke—talking, perhaps you might say, through Burke's hat—if one were to say that the war found chivalry alive and left it dead. Chivalry is about as likely to perish as brown eyes or the moon. Yet something did happen, during the war, to which these wild words would have some sort of relation. We were not all Bayards in 1914; even then a great part of our Press could not tell indignation from spite, nor uphold the best cause in the world without turpitude. Nor were we all, after the Armistice, rods of the houses of Thersites and Cleon; Haig was still alive, and so were Gough and Hamilton and thousands of Arthurian subalterns and privates and of like-minded civilians, though it is harder for a civilian not to lose generosity during a war. But something had happened; the chivalrous temper had had a set-back; it was no longer the mode; the latest wear was a fine robust shabbiness. All through the war there had been a bear movement in Newbolts and Burkes, and, corresponding to this, a bull movement in stocks of the Little Flanigan group.

Chapter XI

STARS IN THEIR COURSES

(1)

'Doth any man doubt,' the wise Bacon asks, 'that if there were taken out of men's minds vain opinions, flattering hopes, false valuations, imaginations as one would, and the like, but it would leave the minds of a number of men poor shrunken things, full of melancholy and indisposition and unpleasing to themselves?' One of the most sweetly flattering hopes that we had in the August of 1914 was that in view of the greatness of the occasion causes were not going to have their effects.

Nothing new, you may truthfully answer, in that. The improvement is one which man, in his cups and his dreams and other seasons of maudlin vision, has always perceived to have just come at last. Now, he exaltedly says to himself, for a clean break with my inadequately wise and brilliant past. Away with that plaguey old list of my things done which should not have been done, and of things left undone which I ought to have done. At the end of popular plays the sympathetic youth who had idled, philandered, or stolen till then would book to the Rand or the Yukon, fully assured that 'in that free, outdoor life' one's character is not one's fate any longer; blessed, 'out there,' are Europe's slackers and wasters, for they shall inherit the earth, or its auriferous parts. Grasshoppers, too, if they drank or resorted to sentimental novels and plays, might have gallant little revolts in their hearts, and chirrup 'Down with causation!' and feel cocksure that some good-natured god would give them a chance of 'redeeming their pasts' quite late in autumn, and put in their way a winter provision far ampler than that which crowns the coolie labours of those sorry daughters of Martha, the bees. But, for working this benign miracle in the soul, no other strong waters can equal the early days of a war. If, with unbecoming sobriety, anyone hints, in such days, that causes may still retain some sort of control, he is easily seen to have no drop of true blood in him;

113

base is the slave who fears we must reap as we sowed; shame upon spiritless whispers about any connection between the making of beds and the lying thereon; now they shall see what excellent hothouse grapes will be borne by the fine healthy thistles that we have been planting and watering.

Something in it too, perhaps—at least some centuries ago. When a great nation's army was only a few thousands strong the freak and the fluke had their chance. An Achilles or two, at the top of their form on the day, might upset the odds. But when armies are millions of men, and machinery counts for more than the men, the few divine accidents of exceptional valour cannot go far. With eleven a-side a Grace or an Armstrong may win a game off his own bat. He will hardly do that in a game where the sides are eleven thousand apiece. More and more, as the armies increase, must the law of averages have it its own dreary way; glorious uncertainties wither; statistical 'curves' of relative national fitness to win, and to stand the strain of winning or losing, overbear everything else. What are the two armies' and the two nations' relative numbers? What is the mean physique on each side? And the mean intelligence? How far has each nation's history—social, political, religious, industrial—tended to make its men rich in just pride, self-reliance, high spirit, devotion, and hardihood? How many per cent on each side have been sapped by venereal disease? How much of their work have its officers troubled to learn? These are the questions. The more men you have in a war, and the longer it lasts, the more completely has it to lose the romance of a glorious gamble and sink—or, as some would say, rise—to the plane of a circumstantial, matter-of-fact liquidation of whatever relative messes the nations engaged have made of the whole of their previous lives.

(II)

Any soldier will tell you the bayonet does not win battles. It only claims, in a way that a beaten side cannot ignore, a victory won already by gunfire, rifles, gas, bombs, or some combination of these. The bayonet's thrust is more of a gesture: a cogent appeal, like the urgent 'How's that?' from the whole of the field when a batsman is almost certainly out. But you may go much further back. That predominant fire itself is just such another appeal. Its greater volume and better direction are only the terms of an army's or a nation's claim to be registered as the winner of what it had really won long ago when, compared with the other nation, it minded its job and lived cleanly and sanely. All war on the new huge scale may be seen as a process, very expensive, of registration or verification. Whenever a war is declared you may say that now, in a sense, it is over at last; all the votes have been cast; the examination papers are written; the time has come for the counting of votes and adjudging of marks. Of course, we may still 'do our bit,' but the possible size of our bit had its limit fixed long ago by the acts of ourselves and our fathers and rulers which made us the men that we are and no more. No use now to try to cadge favour with any *ad hoc* God of Battles. For this, of all gods, is the most dourly Protestant. No squaring of him on the deathbeds of people who would not work while it was yet light.

From many points in the field—some of the best were in the tops of high trees on high ground—you could watch through your glass the casting up of accounts. You might survey from beginning to end a British attack up a bare opposite slope, perhaps with home troops on the left and Canadian or Australasian troops on the right. You had already seen them meet on roads in the rear: battalions of colourless, stunted, half-toothless lads from hot, humid Lancashire mills; battalions of slow, staring faces, gargoyles out of the tragical-comical-historical-pastoral edifice of modern English rural life; Dominion battalions of men startlingly taller, stronger, handsomer, prouder, firmer in nerve, better schooled, more boldly interested in life, quicker to take means to an end and to parry and counter any new blow of circumstance, men who had learned already to look at our men with the half-curious, half-pitying look of a higher, happier caste at a lower. And now you saw them, all these kinds, arise in one continuous line out of the earth and walk forward to bear in the riddled flesh and wrung spirit the sins of their several fathers, pastors, and masters.

Time after time there would come to the watching eye, to the mind still desperately hugging the hope that known causes might not bring their normal effects, the same crushing demonstration

that things are as we have made them. Sometimes the line of
home troops would break into gaps and bunches, lose touch and
direction and common purpose, some of the knots plunging on
into the back of our barrage or feasting some enemy machine-
gunner on their density, others straggling back to the place
whence they had started, while the Dominion troops still ambled
steadily on, their line delicately waving but always continuous,
closing again, as living flesh closes over a pinprick, wherever an
enemy shell tore a hole.

Perhaps the undersized boys from our slums and the under-
witted boys from the 'agricultural, residential, and sporting
estates' of our auctioneers' advertisements would get to their goal,
the spirit wresting prodigies of valour out of the wronged flesh,
hold on there for an hour or two with the shells splashing the
earth up about them like puddle water when great rain-drops
make its surface jump, and then fall back under orders, without
any need, the brain of our army failing to know how to use what
its muscle had won. Then, while you saw the triumphant
Australians throw back a protective flank from the left of their
newly-won front to the English right, far in the rear, you knew
bitterly what the Australians were saying once more: 'They've
let us down again!' 'Another Tommy officer who didn't know
he'd won!' As if it were the fault, that day, of anyone there! Our
men could only draw on such funds of nerve and physique,
knowledge and skill, as we had put into the bank for them. Not
they, but their rulers and 'betters,' had lost their heads in the joy
of making money fast out of steam, and so made half of our
nation slum-dwellers. It was not they who had moulded English
rustic life to keep up the complacency of sentimental modern
imitators of feudal barons. It was not they who had made our
Regular Army neither aristocratic, with the virtues of aristocracy,
nor democratic, with the different virtues of democracy, nor
keenly professional, with the professional virtues of gusto and
curiosity about the possibilities of its work. *Delicta majorum
immeritus lues.* Like the syphilitic children of some jolly Victorian rake, they could only bring to this harsh examination such
health and sanity as all the pleasant vices of Victorian and
Edwardian England had left them.

(III)

The winter after the battle of Loos a sentry on guard at one part
of our line could always see the frustrate skeletons of many
English dead. They lay outside our wire, picked clean by the
rats, so that the khaki fell in on them loosely—little heaps of
bone and cloth half hidden now by nettles and grass. If the
sentry had been a year in the army he knew well enough that
they had gone foredoomed into a battle lost before a shot was
fired. After the Boer War, you remember, England, under the
first shock of its blunders, had tried to find out why the Staff
work was so bad. What it found, in the words of a famous Report, was that the fashion in sentiment in our Regular Army was
to think hard work 'bad form'; a subaltern was felt to be a bit
of a scrub if he worried too much about discovering how to
support an attack when he might be more spiritedly employed
in playing polo; 'The nobleness of life,' as Antony said, when he
kissed Cleopatra, was to go racing or hunting, not to sit learning
how to forecast the course of great battles and how to provide
for answering their calls. And so the swathes of little brown
bundles, with bones showing through, lay in the nettles and grass.

Consider the course of the life of the British Regular officer as
you had known him in youth—not the pick, the saving few, the
unconquerably sound and keen, but the average, staple article
made by a sleek, complacent, snobbish, safe, wealth-governed
England after her own image. Think of his school; of the mystic
aureole of quasi-moral beauty attached by authority there to
absorption in the easy thing—in play; the almost passionate adora-
tion of all those energies and dexterities which, in this world of
evolution towards the primacy of the acute, full brain, are of the
least possible use as aids to survival in men and to victory in
armies. Before he first left home for school he may have been a
normal child who only craved to be given some bit, any odd bit,
of 'real work,' as an experience more thrilling than games. Like
most children, he may have had a zestful command of fresh,
vivid, personal speech, his choice of words expressing simply and
gaily the individual working of his mind and his joy in its work.
Through easy contact with gardeners, gamekeepers, and village

boys he often had established a quite natural, unconscious friend-
liness with people of different social grades. He was probably
born of the kind that pries young, that ask, when they play on
sea sands, why there are tides, and what goes on in the sky that
there should be rain. And then down came the shades of the
prison-house. To make this large, gay book of fairy tales, the
earth, dull and stale to a child importunately fingering at its
covers might seem a task to daunt the strongest. But many of the
teachers of our youth are indomitable men. They can make
earth's most ardent small lover learn from a book what a bore his
dear earth can be, with her strings of names of towns, rivers, and
lakes, her mileages *à faire mourir*, and her insufferable tale of flax
and jute. With an equal firmness your early power of supple and
bright-coloured speech may be taken away and a rag-bag of
feeble stock phrases, misfits for all your thoughts, and worn dull
and dirty by everyone else, be forced upon you instead of the
treasure you had. You may leave school unable to tell what stars
are about you at night or to ask your way to a journey's end in
any country but your own. Between your helpless mind and most
of your fellow-countrymen thick screens of divisions are drawn,
so that when you are fifteen you do not know how to speak to
them with a natural courtesy; you have a vague idea that they
will steal your watch if you leave it about. Above all, you have
learnt that it is still 'bad form' to work; that the youth with brains
and no money may well be despised by the youth with money
and no brains; that the absorbed student or artist is ignoble or
grotesque; that to be able to afford yourself 'a good time' is a
natural title to respect and regard; and that to give yourself any
'good time' that you can is an action of spirit. So it went on at
prep. school, public school, Sandhurst, Camberley. That was how
Staff College French came to be what it was. And as it was what
it was, you can guess what Staff College tactics and strategy
were, and why all the little brown bundles lay where they did
in the nettles and grass.

(IV)

You are more aware of the stars in war than in peace. A full
moon may quite halve the cares of a sentry; the Pole Star will

sometimes be all that a company has, when relieved, to guide it back across country to Paradisiac rest; sleeping often under the sky, you come to find out for yourself what nobody taught you at school—how Orion is sure to be not there in summer, and Aquila always missing in March, and how the Great Bear, that was straight overhead in the April nights, is wont to hang low in the north in the autumn. Childish as it may seem to the wise, a few years' nightly view of these and other invariable arrangements may give a simple soul a surprisingly lively twinge of what the ages of faith seem to have meant by the fear of God— the awesome suspicion that there is some sort of fundamental world order or control which cannot by any means be put off or dodged or bribed to help you to break its own laws. 'Anything,' the old Regular warrant-officers say, 'can be wangled in the army,' but who shall push the Dragon or the Great Dog off his beat? And—who knows?—that may be only a part of a larger system of cause and effect, all of it as hopelessly undodgable.

These apprehensions were particularly apt to arise if you had spent an hour that day in seeing herds of the English 'common people' ushered down narrowing corridors of barbed wire into some gap that had all the German machine guns raking its exit, the nature of Regular officers' pre-war education in England precluding the prompt evolution of any effectual means on our side to derange the working of this ingenious abattoir. We had asked for it all. We had made the directing brains of our armies the poor things that they were. Small blame to them if in this season of liquidation they failed to produce assets which we had never equipped them to earn—mental nimbleness, powers of individual observation, quickness to cap with counter-strokes of invention each new device of the fertile specialists opposite. Being as we had moulded them, they had probably done pretty well in doing no worse.

> *What's* done *we partly may compute,*
> *But know not what's* resisted.

Who shall say what efforts it may have cost some of those poor custom-ridden souls not to veto, for good and all, an engine of war so far from 'smart' as the tank, or to accept any help at all from such folk as the new-fangled, untraditional airmen, some

of whom took no shame to go forth to the fray in pyjamas. Not
they alone, but all of ourselves, with our boastful chatter about
the 'public school spirit,' our gallant, robust contempt for 'swats'
and 'smugs' and all who invented new means to new ends and
who trained and used their brains with a will—we had arranged
for these easy battues of thousands of Englishmen, who, for their
part, did not fail. To-morrow you would see it all again—a few
hundred square yards of ground gained by the deaths, perhaps, of
twenty thousand men who would

> *Go to their graves like beds, fight for a plot*
> *Which is not tomb enough and continent*
> *To hide the slain.*

So it would go on, week after week, sitting after sitting of the
dismal court that liquidated in the Flanders mud our ruling
classes' wasted decades, until we either lost the war outright or
were saved from utter disaster by clutching at aid from French
brains and American numbers. Like Lucifer when he was con-
fronted with the sky at night, you 'looked and sank.'

> *Around the ancient track marched, rank on rank,*
> *The army of unalterable law.*

What had we done, when we could, that the stars in their courses
should fight for us now? Or left undone, of all that could pro-
voke this methodical universe of swinging and returning forces
to shake off such dust from its constant wheels?

(V)

'I planted a set of blind hopes in their minds,' said Prometheus,
making it out to be quite a good turn that he had done to mankind. And the Dr Relling of Ibsen, a kind of Prometheus in
general practice, kept at hand a whole medicine-chest of assorted
illusions to dope his patients with. 'Illusion, you know,' said this
sage, 'is the tonic to give 'em.' It may be. But even illusions
cost something. The bill, as Hotspur said of the river Trent,
'comes me cranking in' presently, nature's iron law laying it down
that the more superb your state of inflation the deeper shall the
dumps occasioned by a puncture be. The Promethean gift of Mr

Dunlop to our race undoubtedly lifted the pastime of cycling out of a somewhat bumpy order of prose into a lyric heaven. And yet the stoutest of all nails could plunge itself into the solid tyre of old without compelling you to walk a foundered Pegasus from the top of the Honister Pass the whole way to Keswick, enjoying *en route* neither the blessing of a bicycle nor that of the unhampered use of Shanks' Mare.

So War, who keeps such a pump to blow you up with, and also such thorns for your puncturing, had to leave us the 'poor shrunken things' that we are, anyhow. It is as if the average man had been passing himself off on himself, in a dream, as the youthful hero of some popular drama, and, in a rousing last act, had departed, in 1914, on excellent terms with himself and the audience, bands playing and flags flying, to start a noble and happy new life on the virgin soil of the 'golden West.' And now he awakes in the 'golden West' on a slobbery and a dirty farm, with all the purchase money still to pay, and tools and manures remarkably dear, and no flag visible, nor instrument of music audible, and dismal reports coming in from neighbouring farmers, and cause and effect as abominably linked one to another as ever, and all the time his mind full of a sour surmise that many sorts of less credulous men have 'made a bit' of inordinate size out of the bit that he did rather than made, during the raging and tearing run of the drama now taken off and, as far as may be, forgotten.

Chapter XII

BELATED BOONS

(I)

THERE is no one day of which you can say: 'My youth ended then. On the Monday the ball of my vision had eagles that flew unabashed to the sun. On the Tuesday it hadn't.' The season of rapture goes out like a tide that has turned; a time has come when the mud flats are bare; but, long after the ebb has set in, any wave that has taken a special strength of its own from some combination of flukes out at sea may cover them up for a moment —may even throw itself far up the beach, making as if to re-capture the lost high-water mark. So the youth of our war had its feints at renewal, hours of Indian summer when there was wine again in the air; in the 'bare, ruined choirs' a lated golden oriole would strike up once more for a while, before leaving.

Because hope does spring eternal the evening before a great battle must always make fires leap up in the mind. The calm before Thermopylæ, the rival camps on the night before Agin-court, the ball before Waterloo—not without reason have writers of genius, searching for glimpses of life in its most fugitive acme of bloom, the poised and just breaking crest of the wave, gone to places and times of the kind. For there the wits and the heart may be really astir and at gaze, and the com-mon man may have, for the hour, the artist's vision of life as an adventure and challenge, lovely, harsh, fleeting, and strange. The great throw, the new age's impending nativity, Fate with her fingers approaching the veil, about to lift—a sense of these things is a drug as strong as strychnine to quicken the failing pulse of the most heart-weary of moribund raptures.

We all had the dope in our wine on the night of August 7, 1918. At daybreak our troops to the east of Amiens would second the first blow of Foch at the German salient towards Paris, the giant arm that was now left sticking out into the air to be hit; its own smashing blow had been struck without killing; its first strength was spent; the spirit behind it was cracking; now, in its moment of check, of lost momentum, or risky extension, now to have at it and smash it. The bull had rushed right on to gore us and missed; we had his flank to stab now.

Some one who dined at the mess had just motored from Paris, through white dust and sunshine and, everywhere, quickly turned heads and eager faces. He had been in the streets all the night of the enemy's last mighty lunge at the city. He spoke of the silent crowds blackening the boulevards through the few hours of midsummer darkness; other crowds on the sky-line of roofs, all black and immobile, the whole city hushed to hear the bombardment, and staring, staring fixedly east at the flame that incessantly winked in the sky above Château-Thierry—history come to life, still enigmatic, but audible, visible, galloping through the night. Poor old France, tormented and stoical, what could not the world forgive her? Then he had seen the news come the next day to these that had thus watched as the non-combatants watched from the high walls of Troy; and how an American had broken down uncontrollably on hearing how his country's Third Division had bundled the Germans back into the Marne: 'We *are* all right! By God, we *are* all right!' he had cried, a whole new nation's secret self-distrust before a supercilious ancient world changing into a younger boy's ecstasy of relief in the thought that now he has jolly well given his proofs and the older boys will not sneer at him now, and he never need bluff any more. Good fellows really, the Yanks; most simple and human as soon as you knew them. One seemed to know everyone then, for that evening.

(II)

Night came on cloudless and windless and braced with autumn's first astringent tang of coolness. Above, as I lay on my back in the meadow, the whole dome had a stir of life in its shimmering fresco, stars flashing and winking with that eager air of having great things to impart—they have it on frosty nights in the Alps, over a high bivouac. We were all worked up, you see. Could it be coming at last, I thought as I went to sleep—the battle unlike other battles? How many I had seen outlive their little youth of groundless hope, from the approach along darkened roads through summer nights, the eastern sky pulsating with its crimson flush, the wild glow always leaping up and always drawing in, and the waiting cavalry's lances upright, black and multitudinous in roadside fields, impaling the blenching sky just above the horizon; and then, in the bald dawn, the backward trickles of wastage swelling into great streams or rather endless friezes seen in silhouette across the fields, the trailing processions of wounded, English and German, on foot and on stretchers, dripping so much blood that some of the tracks were flamboyantly marked for miles across country; and then the evening's reports, with their anxious efforts to show that we had gained something worth having. Was it to be only Loos and the Somme and Arras and Flanders and Cambrai, all over again?

Thought must have passed into dream when I was awakened by some bird that may have had a dream too and had fallen right off its perch in a bush near my head, with a disconcerted squeak and a scuffling sound among dry leaves. Opening my eyes, I found that a thickish veil was drawn over the stars. When I sat up the veil was gone; my eyes were above it; a quilt of white mist, about a foot thick, had spread itself over the meadow. Good! Let it thicken away and be shoes of silence and armour of darkness at dawn for our men. Soon night's habitual sounds brought on sleep again. An owl in the wood by the little chalk stream would hoot, patiently wait for the answering call that should come, and then hoot again, and listen again. The low, dry, continuous buzz of an aeroplane engine, more evenly humming than any of ours, droned itself into hearing and softly ascended the scale of audibility; overhead, as the enemy passed, was slowly drawn across the sky from east to west a line of momentarily obscured stars, each coming back into sight as the next one was deleted. In the east the low, slow grumbling sound of a few guns from fifty miles of front seemed, in its approach to quietude, like the audible breath of a sleeper. The war was taking its rest.

Some sort of musing half-dream about summer heaths, buzzing with bees, was jarred by the big blunted sound, distant and dull, of wooden boxes tumbling down wooden stairs, 'off,' as they do in a farce. Of course—that night-bomber unloading on St Omer, Abbeville, Etaples, some one of the usual marks. But now there was something to wake for. Not a star to be seen. I jumped up and found the mist thick to my armpits, and rising. Oh, good, good! Our men would walk safe as the attacking Germans had walked in the mist of that lovely and fatal morning in March. I slept hard till two o'clock came—time to get up for work. The mist was doing its best; it seemed to fill the whole wide vessel of the universe.

(III)

Ten miles to the east of Amiens a steep-sided ridge divides the converging rivers of Ancre and Somme. They meet where it sinks, at its western end, into the plain. From the ridge there was, in pre-war days, a beautiful view. On the south the ground fell from your feet abruptly, a kind of earth cliff, to the north bank of the Somme, about a hundred feet below. Southwards, beyond the river, stretched, as far as eye could see, the expanse of the level Santerre, one of France's best cornlands. South-east-ward you looked up the Somme valley, mile after mile, towards Bray and Péronne—a shining valley of poplars and stream and linked ponds and red-roofed villages among the poplars. But now the Santerre lay untilled, gone back to heath of a faded fawn-grey. The red roofs had been shelled; the Germans possessed them; the Germans held the blasted heath, across the river; other Germans held most of the ridge on this side to a mile or so east of the point to which I was posted that morning. English troops were to carry the eastern end of the ridge and the tricky low ground between it and the Somme. Australian and Canadian troops were to attack on a broad front, out on the level Santerre, across the river and under our eyes.

But there was no seeing. The mist, in billowy, bolster-like masses, wallowed and rolled about at the touch of light airs; at one moment a figure some thirty yards off could be seen and then a thickened whiteness would rub it out; down the earth cliff we looked into a cauldron of that seething milky opaque-ness. Of what might go on in that pit of enigma the eye could tell nothing; the mind hung on what news might come through the ear. We knew that there was to be no prior bombardment; the men would start with the barrage and go for five miles across the

Santerre if they could, pushing the enemy off it. The stage was set, the play of plays was about to begin on the broad stage below; only, between our eyes and the boards there was hung a white curtain.

Up the cliff, fumbling and muted, came the first burst of the barrage, suggesting, as barrages usually do, a race between sounds, a piece bangingly played against time on a keyboard. Now the men would be rising full length above earth and walking out with smoking breath and bejewelled eyebrows into the infested mist. Then our guns, for an interval, fell almost silent—first lift of the barrage—a chance for hungry ears to assess the weight of the enemy's answering gunfire. Surely, surely it had not all the volume it had had at Arras and Ypres last year. And then down came our barrage again, like one rifle-bolt banging home, and all thought was again with the friends before whose faces the wall of splashing metal, earth, and flame had just risen and moved on ahead like the pillars of fire and cloud.

Hours passed, bringing the usual changes of sounds in battles. The piece that had started so rapidly on the piano slowed down; the notes spaced themselves out; the first continuous barking of many guns slackened off irregularly into isolated barks and groups of barks—just what you hear from a dog whose temper is subsiding, with occasional returns. That, in itself, told nothing. Troops might only have gained a few hundred yards in the old Flanders way, and then flopped down to dig and be murdered. Or—but one kept a tight hand on hope. One had hoped too often since Loos. And then the mist lifted. It rolled right up into the sky in one piece, like a theatre curtain, almost suddenly taking its white quilted thickness away from between our eyes and the vision so much longed for during four years. Beyond the river a miracle—*the* miracle—had begun. It was going on fast. Remember that all previous advances had gained us little more than freedom to skulk up communication trenches a mile or two further eastward, if that. But now! Across the level Santerre, which the sun was beginning to fill with a mist-filtered lustre, two endless columns of British guns, wagons, and troops were marching steadily east, unshelled, over the ground that the Germans had held until dawn.

Nothing like it had ever been seen in the war. Above, on our cliff, we turned and stared at each other. We must have looked rather like Cortes' men agape on their peak. The marvel seemed real; the road lay open and dry across the Red Sea. Far off, six thousand yards off in the shining south-east, tanks and cavalry were at work, shifting and gleaming and looking huge on the sky-line of some little rumpled fold of the Santerre plateau. Nearer, the glass could make out an enemy battery, captured complete, caught with the leather caps still on the muzzles of guns. The British dead on the plain, horses and men, lay scattered thinly over wide spaces; scarcely a foundered tank could be seen; the ground had turf on it still; it was only speckled with shell-holes, not disembowelled or flayed. The war had put on a sort of benignity, coming out gallantly on the top of the earth and moving about in the air and the sun; the warm heath, with so few dead upon it, looked almost clement and kind, almost gay after the scabrous mud wastes and the stink of the captured dug-outs of the Salient, piled up to ground-level with corpses, some feet uppermost, some heads, like fish in a basket, making you think what wonderful numbers there are of mankind. For a moment, the object of all dream and desire seemed to have come; the flaming sword was gone, and the gate of the garden open.

Too late, as you know. We awoke from delight, and remembered. Four years ago, three years ago, even two years ago, a lasting repose of beautitude might have come with that regaining of paradise! Now! The control of our armies, jealously hugged for so long and used, on the whole, to so little purpose, had passed from us, thrown up in a moment of failure, dissension and dread. While still outnumbered by the enemy we had not won; while on even terms with him we had not won; only under a foreign Commander-in-Chief, and with America's inexhaustible numbers crowding behind to hold up our old arms, had our just cause begun to prevail. And now the marred triumph would leave us jaded and disillusioned, divided, half bankrupt; sneerers at lofty endeavour, and yet not the men for the plodding of busy and orderly peace; bilious with faiths and enthusiasms gone sour in the stomach. That very night I was to hear the old Australian sneer again. The British corps on their left, at work in the twisty valley and knucklesome banks of the Somme, had failed to get on quite as fast as they and the Canadian troops on

their right. 'The Canadians were all right, of course, but the
Tommies! Well, we might have known!' They had got rid, they
chuckingly said, of their own last 'Tommy officers' now; they
wanted to have it quite clear that in England's war record they
were not involved except as our saviours from our sorry selves.

(IV)

There were other days, during the following months of worm-
eaten success, when some mirage of the greater joys which we
had forfeited hung for a few moments over the sand. It must
be always a strange delight to an infantryman to explore at his
ease, in security, ground that to him has been almost as un-
imaginable as events after death. There is no describing the
vesture of enigmatic remoteness enfolding a long-watched enemy
line. Tolstoy has tried, but even he does not come up to it. Vergil
alone has expressed one sensation of the British overflow over
Lille and Cambrai, Menin (even the Menin Road had an end)
and Bruges and Ostend, Le Cateau and Landrecies, Liège and
Namur—

> *Juvat ire et Dorica castra*
> *Desertosque videre locos, litusque relictum.*
> *Classibus hic locus, hic acie certare solebant,*
> *Hic Dolopum manus, hic saevus tendebat Achilles.*

And then, wherever you went, till the frontier was reached,
everyone was your host and your friend; all the relations of
strangers to one another had been transfigured into the sum of
all kindness and courtesy. In one mining village in Flanders,
quitted that day by the Germans, a woman rushed out of a house
to give me a lump of bread, thinking that we must all be as
hungry as she and her neighbours. Late one night in Brussels, just
after the Germans had gone, I was walking with another officer
down the chief street of the city, then densely crowded with
radiant citizens. My friend had a wooden stump leg and could
not walk very well; and this figure of a khaki-clad man, maimed
in the discharge of an Allied obligation to Belgium, seemed suddenly and almost simultaneously to be seen by the whole of that
great crowd in all its symbolic value, so that the crowd fell silent

and opened out spontaneously along the whole length of the street and my friend had to hobble down the middle of a long avenue of bare-headed men and bowing women.

Finally—last happy thrill of the war—the first stroke of eleven o'clock, on the morning of Armistice Day, on the town clock of Mons, only captured that morning; Belgian civilians and British soldiers crowding together into the square, shaking each other's hands and singing each other's national anthems; a little toy-like peal of bells in the church contriving to tinkle out 'Tipperary' for our welcome, while our airmen, released from their labours, tumbled and romped overhead like boys turning cartwheels with ecstasy.

What a victory it might have been—the real, the Winged Victory, chivalric, whole and unstained! The bride that our feck-less wooing had sought and not won in the generous youth of the war had come to us now: an old woman, or dead, she no longer refused us. We had arrived, like the prince in the poem—

> *Too late for love, too late for joy,*
> *Too late, too late!*
> *You loitered on the road too long,*
> *You trifled at the gate:*
> *The enchanted dove upon her branch*
> *Died without a mate;*
> *The enchanted princess in her tower*
> *Slept, died behind the grate:*
> *Her heart was starving all this while*
> *You made it wait.*

E

Chapter XIII

THE OLD AGE OF THE WAR

(1)

MEN wearying in trenches used to tell one another sometimes
what they fancied the end of the war would be like. Each had
his particular favourite vision. Some morning the Captain would
come down the trench at 'stand-to' and try to speak as if it were
nothing. 'All right, men,' he would say, 'you can go across and
shake hands.' Or the first thing we should hear would be some
jubilant peal suddenly shaken out on the air from the nearest
standing church in the rear. But the commonest vision was that
of marching down a road to a wide, shining river. Once more the
longing of a multitude struggling slowly across a venomous
wilderness fixed itself on the first glimpse of a Jordan beyond; for
most men the Rhine was the physical goal of effort, the term of
endurance, the symbol of all attainment and rest.

To win what your youth had desired, and find the taste of it
gone, is said to be one of the standard pains of old age. With a
kind of blank space in their minds where the joy of fulfilment
ought to have been, two British privates of 1914, now Captains
attached to the Staff, emerged from the narrow and crowded
High Street of Cologne on December 7, 1918, crossed the Cathedral square, and gained their first sight of the Rhine. As they
stood on the Hohenzollern bridge and looked at the mighty
breadth of rushing stream, each of them certainly gave his heart
leave to leap up if it would and if it could. Had they not, by
toil and entreaty, gained permission to enter the city with our
first cavalry? Were they not putting their lips to the first glass of
the sparkling vintage of victory? Neither of them said anything
then. The heart that knoweth its own bitterness need not always
avow it straight off. But they were friends; they told afterwards.

The first hours of that ultimate winding-up of the old, long-
decaying estate of hopes and illusions were not the worst, either
The cavalry brigadier in command at Colgne, those few first days,

was a man with a good fighting record; and now his gesture towards the conquered was that of the happy warrior, that of Virgilian Rome, that of the older England in hours of victory. German civilians clearly expected some kind of maltreatment, such perhaps as their own scum had given to Belgians. They strove with desperate care to be correct in their bearing, neither to jostle us accidentally in the streets nor to shrink away from us pointedly. Soon, to their surprise and shame, they found that among the combatant English there lingered the hobby of acting like those whom the Germans had known through their Shakespeare: 'We give express charge that in our marches through the country there be nothing compelled from the villages, nothing taken but paid for, none of the French upbraided or abused in disdainful language.'

The 'cease fire' order on Armistice Day had forbidden all 'fraternizing.' But any man who has fought with a sword, or its equivalent, knows more about that than the man who has only blown with a trumpet. To men who for years have lived like foxes or badgers, dodging their way from each day of being alive to the next, there comes back more easily, after a war, a sense of the tacit league that must, in mere decency, bind together all who cling precariously to life on a half-barren ball that goes spinning through space. All castaways together, all really marooned on the one desert island, they know that, however hard we may have to fight to sober a bully or guard to each man his share of the shell-fish and clams, we all have to come back at last to the joint work of making the island more fit to live on. The gesture of the decimated troops who held Cologne at the end of that year was, in essence, that of the cavalry brigadier. Sober or drunk, the men were contumaciously sportsmen, incorrigibly English. One night before Christmas I thought I heard voices outside my quarters long after curfew, and went to look out from my balcony high up in the Domhof into the moon-flooded expanse of the Cathedral square below. By rights there should have been no figures there at that hour, German or British. But there were three; two tipsy Highlanders—'Women from Hell,' as German soldiers used to call the demonic stabbers in kilts—gravely dispensing the consolations of chivalry to a stout burgher of Cologne. 'Och, dinna tak' it to hairrt, mon. I tell ye

E*

that your lads were grond.' It was like a last leap of the flame that had burnt clear and high four years before.

(II)

For the day of the fighting man, him and his chivalric hobbies, was over. The guns had hardly ceased to fire before from the rear, from the bases, from London, there came flooding up the braves who for all those four years had been squealing threats and abuse, some of them begging off service in arms on the plea that squealing was indispensable national work. We had not been long in Cologne when there arrived in hot haste a young press-man from London, one of the first of a swarm. He looked a fine strong man. He seemed to be one of the male Vestals who have it for their trade to feed the eternal flame of hatred between nations, instead of cleaning out stables or doing some other work fit for a male. His train had fortunately brought him just in time for luncheon. This he ate and drank with goodwill, complaining only that the wine, which seemed to me good, was not better. He then slept on his bed until tea-time. Reanimated with tea, he said genially, 'Well, I must be getting on with my mission of hate,' and retired to his room to write a vivacious account of the wealth and luxury of Cologne, the guzzling in all cafés and restaurants, the fair round bellies of all the working class, the sleek and rosy children of the poor. I read it, two days after, in his paper. Our men who had helped to fight Germany down were going short of food at the time, through feeding the children in houses where they were billeted. 'Proper Zoo there is in this place,' one of them told me. 'Proper lions and tigers. Me and my friend are taking the kids from our billet soon's we've got them fatted up a bit. If you'll believe me, sir, them kiddies ain't safe in a Zoo. They could walk in through the bars and get patting the lions.' I had just seen some of the major carnivora in their cages close to the Rhine, each a rectangular lamina of fur and bone like the tottering cats I had seen pass through incredible slits of space in Amiens a month after the people had fled from the city that spring. But little it mattered in London what he or I saw. The nimble scamps had the ear of the world; what the soldier said was not evidence.

Some Allied non-combatants did almost unthinkable things in the first ecstasy of the triumph that others had won. One worthy drove into Cologne in a car plastered over with Union Jacks, like a minor bookie going to Epsom. It passed the wit of man to make him understand that one does not do these things to defeated peoples. But he could understand, with some help, that our Commander-in-Chief alone was entitled to carry a Union Jack on his car. 'We must show these fellows our power'; that was the form of the licence taken out by every churl in spirit who wanted to let his coltish nature loose on a waiter or barber in some German hotel. I saw one such gallant assert the majesty of the Allies by refusing to pay more than half the prices put down on the wine-list. Another would send a waiter across an hotel dining-room to order a quiet party of German men and women not to speak so loud. Another was all for inflicting little bullying indignities on the editor of the *Kölnische Zeitung*—making him print as matters of fact our versions of old cases of German misconduct, etc. Probably he did not even know that the intended exhibition-ground for these deplorable tricks was one of the great journals of Europe.

Not everybody, not even every non-combatant in the dress of a soldier, had caught that shabby epidemic of spite. But it was rife. It had become a fashion to have it, as in some raffish circles it is a fashion at times to have some rakish disease. In the German military cemetery at Lille I have heard a man reared at one of our most famous public schools and our most noble university, and then wearing our uniform, say that he thought the French might do well to desecrate all the German soldiers' graves on French soil. Another, at Brussels, commended a Belgian who was said to have stripped his wife naked in one of the streets of that city and cut off her hair on some airy suspicion of an affair with a German officer during the enemy's occupation. A fine sturdy sneer at the notion of doing anything chivalrous was by this time the mode. 'I hope to God,' an oldish and highly non-combatant general said, in discussing the probable terms of peace with a younger general who had begun the war as a full lieutenant and fought hard all the way up, 'that there's going to be no rot about not kicking a man when he's down.' The junior general grunted. He did not agree. But he clearly felt shy of protesting. Worshippers of setting suns feel ill at ease in discussion with these bright, confident fellows who swear by the rising one.

(III)

The senior general need not have feared. The generous youth of the war, when England could carry, with no air of burlesque, the flag of St George, was pretty well gone. The authentic flame might still flicker on in the minds of a few tired soldiers and disregarded civilians. Otherwise it was as dead as the half-million of good fellows whom it had fired four years ago, whose credulous hearts the maggots were now eating under so many shining and streaming square miles of wet Flanders and Picardy. They gone, their war had lived into a kind of dotage ruled by mean fears and desires. At home our places of honour were brown with shirkers masquerading in the dead men's clothes and licensed by careless authorities to shelter themselves from all danger under the titles of Colonel, Major, and Captain. Nimble politicians were rushing already to coin into votes for themselves—'the men who won the war'—the golden memory of the dead before the living could come home and make themselves heard. Sounds of a general election, the yells of political cheap-jacks, the bawling of some shabby promise, capped by some shabbier bawl, made their way out to Cologne.

'This way, gents, for the right sort of whip to give Germans!' 'Rats, gentlemen, rats! Don't listen to *him*. Leave it to me and I'll chastise 'em with scorpions.' 'I'll devise the brave punishments for them.' 'Ah, but I'll sweat you more money out of the swine.' That was the gist of the din that most of the gramophones of the home press gave out on the Rhine. Each little demagogue had got his little pots of pitch and sulphur on sale for the proper giving of hell to the enemy whom he had not faced. Germany lay at our feet, a world's wonder of downfall, a very Lucifer, fallen, broken, bereaved beyond all the retributive griefs which Greek tragedy shows you afflicting the great who were insolent, wilful, and proud. But it was not enough for our small epicures of revenge. They wanted to twist the enemy's wrists, where he lay bound, and to run pins into his eyes. And they had the upper hand of us now. The soldiers could only look on while the scurvy performance dragged itself out till the meanest of treaties was signed at Versailles. 'Fatal Versailles!' as General Sir Ian Hamilton said for us all; 'Not a line—not one line in your treaty to show that those boys (our friends who were dead) had been any better than the emperors; not one line to stand for the kindliness of England; not one word to bring back some memory of the generosity of her sons!'

'The freedom of Europe,' 'The war to end war,' 'The overthrow of militarism,' 'The cause of civilization'—most people believe so little now in anything or anyone that they would find it hard to understand the simplicity and intensity of faith with which these phrases were once taken among our troops, or the certitude felt by hundreds of thousands of men who are now dead that if they were killed their monument would be a new Europe not soured or soiled with the hates and greeds of the old. That the old spirit of Prussia might not infest our world any more; that they or, if not they, their sons might breathe a new, cleaner air they had willingly hung themselves up to rot on the uncut wire at Loos or wriggled to death, slow hour by hour, in the cold filth at Broodseinde. Now all was done that man could do, and all was done in vain. The old spirit of Prussia was blowing anew, from strange mouths. From several species of men who passed for English—as mongrels, curs, shoughs, water-rugs, and demi-wolves are all clept by the name of dogs—there was rising a chorus of shrill yelps for the outdoing of all the base folly committed by Prussia when drunk with her old conquest of France. Prussia, beaten out of the field, had won in the souls of her conquerors' rulers; they had become her pupils; they took her word for it that she, and not the older England, knew how to use victory.

(IV)

Sir Douglas Haig came to Cologne when we had been there a few days. On the grandiose bridge over the Rhine he made a short speech to a few of us. Most of it sounded as if the thing were a job he had got to get through with, and did not much care for. Perhaps the speech, like those of other great men who wisely hate making speeches, had been written for him by somebody else. But once he looked up from the paper and put in some words which I felt sure were his own; 'I only hope that, now we have won, we shall not lose our heads, as the Germans did after 1870. It has brought them to this.' He looked at the gigantic mounted statue of the Kaiser overhead, a thing crying out in its pride for fire from heaven to fall and consume it, and at the homely, squat British sentry moving below on his post. I think the speech was reported. But none of our foremen at home took any notice of it at all. They knew a trick worth two of Haig's. They were as moonstruck as any victorious Prussian.

So we had failed—had won the fight and lost the prize; the garland of the war was withered before it was gained. The lost years, the broken youth, the dead friends, the women's over-shadowed lives at home, the agony and bloody sweat—all had gone to darken the stains which most of us had thought to scour out of the world that our children would live in. Many men felt, and said to each other, that they had been fooled. They had believed that their country was backing them. They had thought, as they marched into Germany, 'Now we shall show old Fritz how you treat a man when you've thrashed him.' They would let him into the English secret, the tip that the power and glory are not to the bully. As some of them looked at the melancholy performance which followed, our Press and our politicians parad-ing at Paris in moral *pickelhauben* and doing the Prussianist goose-step by way of *pas de triomphe*, they could not but say in dismay to themselves: 'This is our doing. We cannot wish the war unwon, and yet—if we had shirked, poor old England, for all we know, might not have come to this pass. So we come home draggle-tailed, sick of the mess that we were unwittingly helping to make when we tried to do well.'

Chapter XIV

OUR MODERATE SATANISTS

(I)

SATANISM is one of the words that most of us simple people have heard others use; we guiltily feel that we ought to know what it means, but do not quite like to ask, lest we expose the nakedness of the land. Then comes Professor Gilbert Murray, one of the few learned men who are able to make a thing clear to people not quite like themselves, and tells us all about it in a cheap, small book, easy to read. It seems that the Satanists, or the pick of the sect, were Bohemian Protestants at the start, and quite plain, poor men from the country.

'Every person in authority met them with rack and sword, cursed their religious leaders as emissaries of the Devil, and punished them for all the things which they considered holy. The earth was the Lord's, and the Pope and Emperor were the vicegerents of God upon the earth. So they were told; and in time they accepted the statement. That was the division of the world. On the one side God, Pope and Emperor, and the army of persecutors; on the other themselves, downtrodden and poor . . .'

How easy to understand! In crude works of non-imagination the wicked, *repente turpissimus*, suddenly says, some fine morning, 'Evil, be thou my good.' In life the conversion is slower. It is a gradual process of coming to feel that what has passed officially as true, right, and worshipful is so implicated in work manifestly dirty, and so easily made to serve the ends of the greedy, lazy, and cruel, that faith in its authenticity has to be given up as not to be squared with the facts of the world. From feeling this it is not a long step to the further surmise that the grand traditional foe of that old moral order of the world, now so severely discredited, may be less black than so lying an artist has painted him. Does he not, anyhow, stand at the opposite pole to that which has just proved itself base? He, too, perhaps, is some help-less butt of the slings and arrows of an enthroned barbarity tormenting the world. The legend about his condign fall from heaven may only be some propagandist lie—all we are suffered to hear about some early crime in the long, beastly annals of govern-mental misdoing. So thought trips, fairly lightly, along till your worthy Bohemian peasant, literal, serious, and straight, like the plain working-man of all countrysides, turns, with a desperate logical integrity and courage, right away from a world order which has called itself divine and shown itself diabolic. He will embrace, in its stead, the only other world order supposed to be extant; the one which the former order called diabolic; at any rate, he has not wittingly suffered any such wrong at its hand as the scourges of Popes and of Emperors. So the plain man emerges a Satanist.

(II)

To-day the convert does not insist upon bearing the new name. He does not, except in the case of a few doctrinaire bigots, repeat any Satanist creed. But in several portions of Europe the war made conversions abound. Imagine the state of mind that it must have induced in many a plain Russian peasant, literal, serious, and straight, like the Bohemian. First the Tsar, in the name of God and of Holy Russia, sent him, perhaps without so much as a rifle, to starve and be shelled in a trench. If he escaped, the Soviet chiefs, in the name of justice, sent him to fight against those for whom the Tsar had made him fight before, while his wife and babies were starved by those whom he had fought both for and against. When his fighting was done he was made, in the name of social right, an industrial conscript or wage-slave. If alive to-day, he is probably overworked and starved, perhaps far from home, his family life broken up, his instinct or right of self-direction ignored or punished as treason by rulers whom he did not choose, his whole country in danger of lapsing into the abject miseries of an uncared-for fowl-run—all brought about in the name of human freedom.

Consider, again, the case of some German or Austrian widow with many young children. The Kaiser's Government, breathing

the most Christian sentiments, gave the Fatherland war in her
time; her husband was killed, her country is ruined, her children
are growing up stunted and marred by all the years of semi-
starvation; the Paris Press is crying out, in the name of moral
order throughout the world, that they ought to be starved more
drastically; part of the English Press complains, in the tone of
an outraged spiritual director, that she has shown no adequate
signs of repentance of the Kaiser's sins, and that she and hers are
living like fighting cocks; the German Agrarian Party, in the
name of Patriotism, manœuvres to keep her from getting her
weekly ounce or two of butcher's meat from abroad more
cheaply than they would like to sell it to her at home.

What could you say to such people if they should break out
at last in despair and defiance: 'Anyhow, all these people, here
and abroad, who take upon themselves to speak for God and duty
and patriotism and liberty and loyalty are evil people, and do
evil things. Shall not all these trees that they swear by be judged
by their fruits? Away with them into the fire, God and country
and social duty and justice and every old phrase that used to
seem more than a phrase till the war came to show it up for
what it was worth as a means to right conduct in men?' Of
course you could say a great deal. But at every third word they
could incommode you with some stumping case of the foulest
thing done in the holiest name till you would be shamed into
silence at the sight of all the crowns of thorns brought to market
by keepers of what you still believe to be vineyards. So, throughout much of Europe, Satan's most promising innings for many
long years has begun.

(III)

In their vices as well as their virtues the English preserve a distinguished moderation. They do not utterly shrink from jobbery,
for example; they do from a job that is flagrant or gross. They
give judgeships as prizes for party support, but not to the utterly
briefless, the dullard who knows no more law than necessity.
Building contractors, when in the course of their rise they become town councillors, do not give bribes right and left: their
businesses thrive without that. An Irishman running a Tammany

in the States cannot thus hold himself in: the humorous side of
corruption charms him too much: he wants to let the grand farce
of roguery rip for all it is worth. But the English private's pet
dictum, 'There's reason in everything,' rules the jobber, the
profiteer, the shirker and placeman of Albion as firmly as it con-
trols the imagination of her Wordsworths and the political ideal-
ism of her Cromwells and Pitts. Like her native cockroaches and
bugs, whose moderate stature excites the admiration and envy of
human dwellers among the corresponding fauna of the tropics,
the caterpillars of her commonwealth preserve the golden mean;
few, indeed, are flamboyants or megalomaniacs.

So, when the war with its great opportunities came we were
but temperately robbed by our own birds of prey. Makers of
munitions made mighty fortunes out of our peril. Still, every
British soldier did have a rifle, at any rate when he went to the
front. I have watched a twelve-inch gun fire, in action, fifteen of
its great bales or barrels of high explosives, fifteen running, and
only three of the fifteen costly packages failed to explode duly on
its arrival beyond. Vendors of soldiers' clothes and boots acquired
from us the wealth which dazzles us all in these days of our own
poverty. They knew how to charge: they made hay with a will
while the blessed suns of 1914-18 were high in the heavens. Still,
nearly all the tunics made in that day of temptation did hold
together; none of the boots, so far as I knew or heard tell, was
made of brown paper. 'He that maketh haste to be rich shall not
be innocent.' Still, there is reason in everything. 'Meden agan,' as
the Greeks said—temperance in all things, even in robbery, even
in patriotism and personal honour. Our profiteers did not bid
Satan get him behind them; but they did ask him to stand a little
to one side.

So, too, in the army. Some old Regular sergeant-majors would
sell every stripe that they could, but they would not sell a map
to the enemy. Some of our higher commanders would use their
A.D.C. rooms as funk-holes to shelter the healthy young nephew
or son of their good friend the earl, or their distant cousin the
marquis. But there were others. Sometimes a part of our Staff
would almost seem to forget the war, and give its undivided mind
to major struggles—its own intestine 'strafes' and the more bitter
war against uncomplaisant politicians at home. But presently it

emperor assailable. I remember a little private, who seemed to know Dickens by heart, applying to William the Second in 1915 the words used by the Game Chicken about Mr Dombey—'as stiff a cove as ever he see, but within the resources of science to double him up with one blow in the waistcoat.' This he proved, too, he and his like, casting down the proud from their seats with little help from all that was highly placed and reverently regarded in his own country. Our ruling class had, on the whole, failed, and had to be pulled through by him and the French and Americans; that feeling, in one form or another, is clear in the common man's mind. He may not know in detail the record of French as commander-in-chief, nor the exact state of the Admiralty which let the *Goeben* and the *Breslau* go free, nor the inner side of the diplomacy which added Turkey, and even Bulgaria, to our enemies, nor yet the well-born underworld of war-time luxury, disloyalty, and intrigue which notorious memoirs have since revealed. But some horse instinct or some pricking in his thumbs told him correctly that in every public service manned mainly by our upper classes the war-time achievement was relatively low. There is very little natural inclination to class jealousy among plain Englishmen. Equalitarian theory does not interest them much. Their general relish for a gamble makes them rather like a lucky-bag or bran-tub society in which anyone may pick up, with luck, a huge unearned prize. By cheerfully helping to keep up the big gaming-hell, by giving Barnatos and Joels pretty full value for their win, the pre-war governing class gained a kind of strength which a prouder and more fastidious aristocracy would have foregone. It stands in little physical danger now. But it lives, since the war, in a kind of contempt. The one good word that the average private had for bestowal among his unseen 'betters' during the later years of the war was for the King. '*He* did give up his beer' was said a thousand times by men whom that symbolic act of willing comradeship with the dry throat on the march and the war-pinched household at home had touched and astonished.

Other institutions, too, had been weighed in the balance. The War Office was only the commonest of many by-words. The Houses of Parliament, in which too many men of military age had demanded the forced enlistment of others, wore an air of insincerity, apart from the loss of prestige inevitable in a war; for armies always take the colour out of deliberative essemblies. To moderate this effect a large number of members who did not go to the war found means to wear khaki in London instead of black, but this well-conceived precaution only succeeded in further curling the lip of derision among actual soldiers. The churches, as we have seen, got their chance, made little or nothing of it, and came out of the war quite good secular friends with the men, but almost null and void in their eyes as ghostly counsellors, and stripped of the vague consequence with which many men had hitherto credited them on account of any divine mission they might be found to have upon closer acquaintance. Respect for the truthfulness of the Press was clean gone. The contrast between the daily events that men saw and the daily accounts that were printed was final. What the Press said thenceforth was not evidence. But still it had sent out plum puddings at Christmas.

Neither was anything evidence now that was said by a politician. A great many plain men had really drawn a distinction, all their lives, between the solemn public assurances of statesmen and the solemn public assurances of men who draw teeth outside dock-gates and take off their caps and call upon God to blast the health of their own darling children if a certain pill they have for sale does not cure colds, measles, ringworm, and the gripes within twenty-four hours of taking. A Swift might say there never was any difference, but the plain man had always firmly believed that there was. Now, after the war, he is shaken. Every disease which victory was to cure he sees raging worse than before: more poverty, less liberty, more likelihood of other wars, more spite between master and man, less national comradeship. And then the crucial test case, the solemn vow of the statesmen, all with their hands on their sleek bosoms, that if only the common man would save them just that once they would turn to and think of nothing else, do nothing else, but build him a house, assure him of work, settle him on land, make all England a paradise for him—a 'land fit for heroes to live in.' And then the sequel: the cold fit; the feint at house-building and its abandonment; all the bankruptcy of promise; the ultimate bilking, done by way of reluctant surrender to 'anti-waste' stunts got up by the same cheap-jacks of the Press who in the first year of the war would have had the statesmen promise yet more wildly than they did. Colds, measles, ringworm, and gripes all flourishing, much more than twenty-four hours after, and new ailments added unto them.

No relief, either, by running from one medicine-man to the next. Few of our disenchanted men doubt that the lightning cure of the Communist is only just another version of the lightning cure of the Tory, the authoritarian, the peremptory regimentalist. 'Give *me* a free hand and all will be well with you.' Both say exactly the same thing in the end. One of them may call it the rule of the fittest, the other the rule of the proletariat; each means exactly the same thing—the rule of himself, the enforcement on everyone else of his own darling theory of what is best for them, whether they know it or not. Small choice is rotten apples; one bellyful of east wind is a diet as poor as another. Not in the yells and counter-yells of this and that vendor of patent hot-air is the heart of the average ex-soldier engaged. Rather 'Away with all gas-projectors alike' is his present feeling towards eloquent men, Left or Right. For the moment he knows them too well, and is tired of hearing of plans which might work if he were either a babe in arms or a Michael of super-angelic wisdom and power.

(V)

You may be disillusioned about the value of things, or about their security, either coming to feel that your house is a poor place to live in or that, pleasant or not, it is likely enough to come down on your head. Of these two forms of discomfort our friend experiences both. Much that he took to be fairly noble now looks pretty mean; and much that seemed reassuringly stable is seen to be shaky. Civilization itself, the at any rate habitable dwelling which was to be shored up by the war, wears a strange new air of precariousness.

Even before the war a series of melancholy public misadventures had gone some way to awake the disquieting notion that civilization, the whole ordered, fruitful joint action of a nation, a continent, or the whole world, was only a bluff. When the world is at peace and fares well, the party of order and decency, justice and mercy and self-control, is really bluffing a much larger party of egoism and greed that would bully and grab if it dared. The deep anti-social offence of the 'suffragettes,' with their hatchets and hunger-strikes, was that they gave away, in some measure, the bluff by which non-criminal people had hitherto kept some control over reluctant assentors to the rule of mutual protection and forbearance. They helped the baser sort to see that the bluff of civilization is at the mercy of anyone ready to run a little bodily risk in calling it. Sir Edward Carson took up the work. He 'called' the bluff of the Pax Britannica, the presumption that armed treason to the law and order of the British Empire must lead to the discomfiture of the traitor, whoever he was; he presented Sinn Fein and every other would-be insurgent with proof that treason may securely do much more than peep at what it would; British subjects, he showed, might quite well conspire for armed revolt against the King's peace and not be any losers, in their own persons, by doing it.

The greatest of all bluffs, the general peace of the world and the joint civilization of Europe, remained uncalled for a year or two more. It was a high moral bluff. People were everywhere saying that world-war was too appalling, too frantically wicked a thing for any government to invite or procure. Peace, they argued, held a hand irresistibly strong. Had she not, among her cards, every acknowledged precept of Christianity and of morality, even of wisdom for a man's self or a nation's? Potsdam called the world's bluff, and the world's hand was found to be empty. Potsdam lost the game in the end, but it had not called wholly in vain. To a Europe exhausted, divided, and degraded by five years of return to the morals of the Stone Age it had suggested how many things are as they are, how many things are owned as they are, how many lives are safely continued, merely because our birds of prey have not yet had the wit to see what would come of a sudden snatch made with a will and with assurance. The total number of policemen on a racecourse is always a minute percentage of the total number of its thieves and roughs. The bad men are not held down by force; they are only bluffed by the pretence of it. They have got the tip now, and the plain man is dimly aware how surprisingly little there is to keep us all from slipping back into the state we were in when

would kill another to steal a piece of food that he had
got, and when a young woman was not safe on a road out of
sight of her friends.

The plain man, so far as I know him, is neither aghast nor
gleeful at this revelation. For the most part he looks somewhat
listlessly on, as at a probable dog-fight in which there is no dog
of his. A sense of moral horror does not come easily when you
have supped full of horrors on most of the days of three or four
years; sacrilege has to go far, indeed, to shock men who have
seen their old gods looking extremely human and blowing out,
one by one, the candles before their own shrines. Some new god,
or devil, of course, may enter at any time into this disfurnished
soul. Genius in some leader might either possess it with an
anarchic passion to smash and delete all the old institutions that
disappointed in the day of trial or fire it with a new craving to
lift itself clear of the wrack and possess itself on the heights. For
either a Lenin or a St Francis there is a wide field to till, cleared,
but of pretty stiff clay. Persistently sane in his disenchantment as
he had been in his rapture, the common man, whose affection and
trust the old order wore out in the war, is still slow to enlist
out-and-out in any Satanist unit. There's reason, he still feels, in
everything. So he remains, for the time, like one of the angels
whom the Renaissance poet represented as reincarnate in man;
the ones who in the insurrection of Lucifer were not for Jehovah
nor yet for his enemy.

Chapter XV

ANY CURE?

(1)

How shall it all be set right? For it must be, of course. A people that did not wait to be pushed off its seat by the Kaiser is not likely now to turn its face to the wall and die inertly of shortage of faith and general moral debility. Some day soon we shall have to cease squatting among the potsherds and crabbing each other, and give all the strength we have left to the job of regaining the old control of ourselves and our fate which, in the days of our health, could only be kept by putting forth constantly the whole force of the will. 'Not to be done,' you may say. And, of course, it will be a miracle. But only the everyday miracle done in some-body's body, or else in his soul. When the skin shines white and tight over the joints, and the face is only a skull with some varieties of expression, and the very flame flickers and jumps in the lamp, the body will bend itself up to expel a disease that it could not, in all its first splendour of health, keep from the door. In all the breeds of cowardly livers—drunkards, thieves, liars, sorners, drug-takers, all the kinds that have run from the enemy, throwing away as they ran every weapon that better men use to repel him—you will find some that turn in the end and rend with their bare hands the fiend that they could not face with their bow and their spear.

But these recoveries only come upon terms: no going back to heaven except through a certain purgatorial passage. There, while it lasts, the invalid must not expect to enjoy either the heady visions of the fever that is now taking its leave or the more temperate beautitude of the health that may presently come. He lies reduced to animal, almost vegetable, matter, quite joyless and unthrilled, and has to abide in numb passivity, like an unborn child's, whatever may come of the million minute molecular changes going on unseen in the enigmatic darkness of his tissues, where tiny cell is adding itself to tiny cell to build he knows not you can; a lie will easily get you out of a scrape, and yet, strangely and beautifully, rapture possesses you when you have taken the scrape and left out the lie. Divine unreason, as little scrutable and yet as surely a friend as the star that hangs a lamp out from the Pole to show you the way across gorse-covered commons in Surrey. So he will toe the line of a duty, not with a mere release from dismay, but exultantly, with the fire and lifting of heart of the strong man and the bridegroom, feeling always the same secret and almost sensuous transport, while he suppresses a base impulse, that he felt when he pressed the warm turf with his hand or the crumbling clay trickled warm between his fingers.

The right education, if we could find it, would work up this creative faculty of delight into all its branching possibilities of knowledge, wisdom, and nobility. Of all three it is the beginning, condition, or raw material. At present it almost seems to be the aim of the commonplace teacher to take it firmly away from any pupil so blessed as to possess it. How we all know the kind of public school master whose manner expresses breezy comradeship with the boys in facing jointly the boredom of admittedly beastly but still unavoidable lessons! And the assumption that life out of school is too dull to be faced without the aid of infinitely elaborated games! And the girl schools where it seems to be feared that evil must come in any space of free time in which neither a game nor a dance nor a concert nor a lecture with a lantern intervenes to rescue the girls from the presumed tedium of mere youth and health! Everywhere the assumption that simple things have failed; that anything like hardy mental living and looking about for oneself, to find interests, is destined to end ill; that the only hope is to keep up the full dose of drugs, to be always pulling and pushing, prompting and coaxing and tickling the youthful mind into condescending to be interested. You know the effects: the adolescent whose mind seems to drop when taken out of the school shafts, or at least to look round, utterly at a loss, with a plaintive appeal for a suggestion of something to do, some excitement to come, something to make it worth while to be alive on this dull earth. We saw the effects in our hapless brain work in the war.

But if we were to wait to save England till thousands of men and women brought up in this way see what they have lost and insist on a better fate for their children we might as well write England off as one with Tyre and Sidon already. Her case is too pressing. She cannot wait for big, slowly telling improvements in big institutions, although improvements must come. She has to be saved by a change in the individual temper. We each have to fall back, with a will, on the only way of life in which the sane simplicity of joy in plain things and in common rightness of action can be generated. Health of mind or body comes of doing wholesome things—perhaps for a long time without joy in doing them, as the sick man lies chafing, eating the slops that are all he is fit for, or as the dipsomaniac drinks in weariness and depression the insipid water that is to save him. Then, on some great day, self-control may cease to be merely the sum of many dreary acts of abstention; it may take life again as an inspiriting force, both a warmth and a light, such as makes nations great.

Chapter XVI

FAIR WARNING

(1)

To give the cure a chance we must have a long quiet time. And we must secure it now.

For the moment, no doubt, war has gone out of fashion; it pines in the shade, like the old horsehair covers for sofas, or anti-macassars of lace. Hardly a day can pass, even now, but someone finds out, with a start and a look of displeasure, that war has been given its chance and has not done quite so well as it ought to have done. One man will write to the Press, in dismay, that the meals in the Simplon Express are not what they were in 1910. Another, outward bound by Calais to Cannes, has found that the hot-water plant in his sleeping-compartment struck work—and that in a specially cold sector down by the Alps. Thus does war, in the end, knock at the doors of us all: like the roll of the earth upon its axis, it brings us, if not death or destitution or some ashy taste in the mouth, at any rate a sense of a fallen temperature in our bunks. However non-porous our minds, there does slowly filter into us the thought that when a million of a country's men of working age have just been killed there may be a plaguey dearth of the man-power needed to keep in pleasant order the lavatories of its *trains de luxe*. Sad to think how many tender minds, formed in those Elysian years—Elysian for anyone who was not poor— before the war, will have to suffer, probably for many years, these little shocks of realization.

Surely there never was any time in the life of the world when it was so good, in the way of obvious material comfort, to be alive and fairly well-to-do as it was before the war. Think of the speed and comfort and relative cheapness of the Orient Express; of the way you could wander, unruined, through long æsthetic holidays in Italy and semi-æsthetic, semi-athletic holidays in the Alps; of the week-end accessibility of London from Northern England; of the accessibility of public schools for the

156

sons of the average parson or doctor; of the penny post, crown
of our civilization—torn from us while the abhorred halfpenny
post for circulars was yet left; of the Income Tax just large
enough to give us a pleasant · sense of grievance patriotically
borne, but not to prostrate us, winter and summer, with two
'elbow jolts' or 'Mary Ann punches' like those of the perfected
modern prize-fighter.

Many sanguine well-to-do people dreamt, in the August of
1914, that the war, besides attaining its primary purpose of beating the enemy, would disarrange none of these blessings; that it
would even have as a by-product a kind of 'old-time Merrie
England,' with the working classes cured of the thirst for wages
and deeply convinced that everyone who was not one of themselves was a natural ruler over them. For any little expense to
which the war might put us the Germans would pay, and our
troops would return home to dismiss all trade-union officials and
to regard the upper and middle classes thenceforth as a race of
heaven-sent colonels—men to be followed, feared, and loved. Ah,
happy vision, beautiful dream!—like Thackeray's reverie about
having a very old and rich aunt. The dreamer awakes among the
snows of the Mont Cenis with a horrid smell in the corridor and
the hot-water pipes out of order. And so war has gone out of
fashion, even among cheery well-to-do people.

(II)

But may it not come into fashion again? Do not all the great
fashions move in cycles, like stars? When our wars with Napoleon were just over, and all the bills still to be paid, and the
number of visibly one-legged men at its provisional maximum,
must not many simple minds have thought that surely man would
never idealize any business so beastly and costly again? And then
see what happened. We were all tranquilly feeding, good as gold,
in the deep and pleasant meadows of the long Victorian peace
when from some of the frailest animals in the pasture there rose a
plaintive bleat for war. It was the very lambs that began it. 'Shall
we never have carnage?' Stevenson, the consumptive, sighed to
a friend. Henley, the cripple, wrote a longing 'Song of the
Sword.' Out of the weak came forth violence. Bookish men be-

gan to hug the belief that they had lost their way in life; they felt that they were Neys or Nelsons *manqués*, or cavalry leaders lost to the world. 'If I had been born a corsair or a pirate,' thought Mr Tappertit, musing among the ninepins, 'I should have been all right.' Fragile dons became connoisseurs, *faute de mieux*, of prize-fighting; they talked, nineteen to the dozen, about the still, strong man and 'straight-flung words and few,' adored 'naked force,' averred they were not cotton-spinners at all, and deplored the cankers of a quiet world and a long peace. Some of them entered quite hotly, if not always expertly, into the joys and sorrows of what they called 'Tommies,' and chafed at the many rumoured refusals of British innkeepers to serve them, little knowing that only by these great acts of renunciation on the part of licensees has many a gallant private been saved from falling into that morgue an 'officer house,' and having his beer congealed in the glass by the refrigerative company of colonels.

The father and mother of this virilistic movement among the well-read were Mr Andrew Lang, the most donnish of wits, and one of the wittiest. Lang would review a new book in a great many places at once. So, when he blessed, his blessing would carry as far as the more wholly literal myrrh and frankincense wafted abroad by the hundred hands of Messers Boot. The fame of Mr Rider Haggard was one of Lang's major products. Mr Haggard was really a man of some mettle. By persons fitted to judge he was believed to have at his fingers' ends all the best of what is known and thought by mankind about turnips and other crops with which they may honourably and usefully rotate. But it was for turning his back upon these humdrum sustainers of life and writing, in a rich Corinthian style, accounts of fancy 'slaughters grim and great,' that his flame lived and spread aloft, as Milton says, in the pure eyes and perfect witness of Lang. Another nursling of Lang's was the wittier Kipling, then a studious youth exuding Border ballads and Bret Harte from every pore, but certified to carry about him, on paper, the proper smell of blood and tobacco.

Deep answered unto deep. In Germany, too, the pibrochs of the professors were rending the skies, and poets of C_4 medical grade were tearing the mask from the hideous face of peace. The din throughout the bookish parts of Central and Western Europe

suggested to an irreverent mind a stage with a quaint figure of
some short-sighted pedagogue of tradition coming upon it,
round-shouldered, curly-toed, print-fed, physically inept, to play
the part of the war-horse in Job, swallowing the ground with
fierceness and rage, and 'saying among the trumpets "Ha, ha!" '
You may see it all as a joke. Or as something rather more than a
joke, in its effects. Mr Yeats suggested that an all-seeing eye
might perceive the Trojan War to have come because of a tune
that a boy had once piped in Thessaly. What if all our millions
of men had to be killed because some academic Struwwelpeter,
fifty years since, took on himself to pipe up 'Take the nasty peace
away!' and kick the shins of Concord, his most kindly nurse?

(III)

If he did, it was natural. All Struwwelpeters are natural. All heirs-
apparent are said to take the opposite side to their fathers still on
the throne. And those learned men were heirs to the age of the
Crystal Palace, the age of the first 'Locksley Hall,' with its
'parliament of man' and 'federation of the world,' the age that laid
a railway line along the city moat of Amiens and opened capa-
cious Hôtels de la Paix throughout Latin Europe, the age when
passports withered and Bædeker was more and more, the age that
in one of its supreme moments of ecstasy founded the London
International College, an English public school (now naturally
dead) in which the boys were to pass some of their terms among
the heathen in Germany or France.

The cause of peace, like all triumphant causes, good as they
may be, had made many second-rate friends. It had become safe,
and even sound, for the worldly to follow. The dullards, the
people who live by phrases alone, the scribes who write by rote
and not with authority—most of these had drifted into its
service. It had become a provocation, a challenge, vexing those
'discoursing wits' who 'count it,' Bacon says, 'a bondage to fix a
belief.' A rebound had to come. And those arch-rebounders were
men of the teaching and writing trades, wherein the newest
fashions in thought are most easily canvassed, and any inveterate
acquiescence in mere common sense afflicts many bosoms with
the fear of lagging yards and yards behind the foremost files of

time; perhaps—that keenest agony—of having nothing piquant or startling to say, no little bombs handy for conversational purposes. 'I sat down,' the deserving young author says in *The Vicar of Wakefield*, 'and, finding that the best things remained to be said on the wrong side, I resolved to write a book that should be wholly new. I therefore dressed up three paradoxes with some ingenuity. They were false, indeed, but they were new. The jewels of truth have been so often imported by others that nothing was left for me to import but some splendid things that, at a distance, looked every bit as well.' 'Peace on earth, goodwill towards men,' 'Blessed are the peacemakers'—these and the like might be jewels; but they were demoded; they were old tags; they were clichés of bourgeois morality; they were *vieux jeu*, like the garnets with which, in *She Stoops to Conquer*, the young woman of fashion declined to be pacified when her heart cried out for the diamonds.

(IV)

Then the Church itself must needs take a hand—or that part of the Church which ever cocks an eye at the latest fashions in public opinion, the 'blessed fellows,' like Poins, that 'think as every man thinks' and help to swell every passing shout into a roar. I find among old papers a letter written in Queen Victoria's reign by an unfashionable curmudgeon whose thought would not keep to the roadway like theirs. 'I see,' this rude ironist writes, 'that "the Church's duty in regard to war" is to be discussed at the Church Congress. That is right. For a year the heads of our Church have been telling us what war is and does—that it is a school of character, that it sobers men, cleans them, strengthens them, knits their hearts, makes them brave, patient, humble, tender, prone to self-sacrifice. Watered by "war's red rain," one bishop tells us, virtue grows; a cannonade, he points out, is an "oratorio"—almost a form of worship. True; and to the Church men look for help to save their souls from starving for lack of this good school, this kindly rain, this sacred music. Congresses are apt to lose themselves in wastes of words. This one must not —surely cannot—so straight is the way to the goal. It has simply to draft and submit a new Collect for "war in our time," and to call for the reverent but firm emendation, in the spirit of the best modern thought, of those passages in Bible and Prayer-book by which even the truest of Christians and the best of men have at times been blinded to the duty of seeking war and ensuing it.

'Still, man's moral nature cannot, I admit, live by war alone. Nor do I say, with some, that peace is wholly bad. Even amid the horrors of peace you will find little shoots of character fed by the gentle and timely rains of plague and famine, tempest and fire; simple lessons of patience and courage conned in the schools of typhus, gout, and stone; not oratorios, perhaps, but homely anthems and rude hymns played on knife and gun, in the long winter nights. Far from me to "sin our mercies" or to call mere twilight dark. Yet dark it may become. For remember that even these poor makeshift schools of character, these second-bests, these halting substitutes for war—remember that the efficiency of every one of them, be it hunger, accident, ignorance, sickness or pain, is menaced by the intolerable strain of its struggle with secular doctors, plumbers, inventors, schoolmasters, and police-men. Every year thousands who would in nobler days have been braced and steeled by manly tussles with smallpox or diphtheria are robbed of that blessing by the great changes made in our drains. Every year thousands of women and children must go their way bereft of the rich spiritual experience of the widow and the orphan. I try not to despond, but when I think of all that Latimer owed to the fire, Regulus to a spiked barrel, Socrates to prison, and Job to destitution and disease—when I think of these things and then think of how many of my poor fellow creatures in our modern world are robbed daily of the priceless discipline of danger, want, and torture, then I ask myself—I cannot help asking myself—whether we are not walking into a very slough of moral and spiritual squalor.

'Once more, I am no alarmist. As long as we have wars to stay our souls upon, the moral evil will not be grave; and, to do the Ministry justice, I see no risk of their drifting into any long or serious peace. But weak or vicious men may come after them, and it is now, in the time of our strength, of quickened insight and deepened devotion, that we must take thought for the leaner years when there may be no killing of multitudes of Englishmen, no breaking up of English homes, no chastening blows to English

trade, no making, by thousands, of English widows, orphans, and
cripples—when the school may be shut and the rain a drought
and the oratorio dumb.'

But what did a few unfashionable curmudgeons count for,
against so many gifted divines?

(V)

And yet all mortal things are subject to decay, even reactions,
even decay itself, and there comes a time when the dead Ophelia
may justly be said to be not decomposing, but recomposing
successfully as violets and so forth. Heirs-apparent grow up into
kings and have little heirs of their own who, hearkening to
nature's benevolent law, become stout counter-reactionists in
their turn. So now the pre-war virilists, the literary braves who
felt that they had supped too full of peace, have died in their
beds, or lost voice, like the cuckoos in June, and a different breed
find voice and pipe up. These are the kind, the numerous kind,
whose youth has supped quite full enough of war. For them
Bellona has not the mystical charm, as of grapes out of reach,
that she had for the Henleys and Stevensons. All the veiled-
mistress business is off. Battles have no aureoles now in the sight
of young men as they had for the British prelate who wrote that
old poem about the 'red rain.' The men of the counter-reaction
have gone to the school and sat the oratorio out and taken a
course of the waters, after the worthy prelate's prescription.
They have seen trenches full of gassed men, and the queue of
their friends at the brothel-door in Bethune. At the heart of the
magical rose was seated an earwig.

Presently all the complaisant part of our Press may jump to
the fact that the game of idealizing war is now, in its turn, a
back number. Then we may hear such a thudding or patter of
feet as Carlyle describes when Louis XV was seen to be dead and
the Court bolted off, *ventre à terre*, along the corridors of
Versailles, to kiss the hand of Louis XVI. And then will come
the season of danger. Woe unto Peace, or anyone else, when all
men speak well of her, even the base. When Lord Robert Cecil
and Mr Clynes and Sir Hubert Gough stand up for the peace
which ex-soldiers desire, it is all right. But what if Tadpole and

Taper stood up for it? What if all the vendors of supposedly popular stuff, all the timid gregarious repeaters of current banalities, all the largest circulations in the solar system were on the side of peace, as well as her old bodyguard of game disregarders of fashion and whimsical stickers-up for Christianity, chivalry, or sportsmanship?

We must remember that, in the course of nature, the proportion of former combatants among us must steadily decline. And war hath no fury like a non-combatant. Can you not already forehear, in the far distance, beyond the peace period now likely to come, the still, small voice of some Henley or Lang of later days beginning to pipe up again with Ancient Pistol's ancient suggestion: 'What? Shall we have incision? Shall we imbrue?' And then a sudden *furore*, a war-dance, a beating of tomtoms. And so the whole cycle revolving again. 'Seest thou not, I say, what a deformed thief this fashion is? How giddily a' turns about all the hot bloods between fourteen and five-and-thirty? Sometimes fashioning them like Pharaoh's soldiers in the reechy painting, sometimes like god Bel's priests in the old church window; sometimes like the shaven Hercules in the smirched worm-eaten tapestry?' Anything to be in the fashion.

There is only one thing for it. There must still be five or six million ex-soldiers. They are the most determined peace party that ever existed in Britain. Let them clap the only darbies they have—the Covenant of the League of Nations—on to the wrists of all future poets, romancers, and sages. The future is said to be only the past entered by another door. We must beware in good time of those boys, and fiery elderly men, piping in Thessaly.